FOREWORD

Spent fuel or high-level radioactive waste is now produced in many countries as a result of the generation of electricity by nuclear reactors. The long periods of time over which this type of waste remains potentially hazardous require a disposal method based on its capability to provide long-term isolation. Burial beneath the ocean floor in geologically stable sediment formations has been studied because of its potential for long-term isolation.

Since 1977, countries conducting research on ocean-floor burial of high-level waste, often called sub-seabed or seabed disposal, have cooperated and exchanged information in the framework of the Seabed Working Group established under the Radioactive Waste Management Committee of the OECD Nuclear Energy Agency. Members of the Group are: Belgium, Canada, France, the Federal Republic of Germany, Italy, Japan, the Netherlands, Switzerland, United Kingdom, United States, and the Commission of the European Communities (CEC).

The objective of the Seabed Working Group is to provide scientific and technical information to enable international and national authorities to assess the safety and engineering feasibility of seabed disposal. As none of the participating countries intend to use seabed disposal in the foreseeable future, the work of the Seabed Working Group should essentially be seen at this stage as a scientific contribution to the identification and assessment of potential methods for radioactive waste disposal.

An Executive Committee guided the overall direction and policy of the Seabed Working Group in this research. Its members represented their respective national programmes, made financial commitments and coordinated national positions in order to permit the Seabed Working Group to pursue its overall objectives. A large number of scientists have contributed to the research which comprises the present body of knowledge relating to seabed disposal of radioactive waste.

This volume is one of a series of eight volumes assessing seabed disposal based on research carried out by the Seabed Working Group over the last ten years. Volume 1 provides an overview of the research and a summary of the results. Volumes 2 to 8 consist of technical supplements which provide a more detailed description of radiological assessment, geoscience characterization, engineering studies and the scientific basis upon which the radiological assessment is built. Although legal, political, and institutional aspects are essential to possible future use of seabed disposal, they are not being considered in this series.

This report represents the views of the authors. It commits neither the Organisation nor the Governments of Member Countries.

SERIES TITLES

GENERAL TITLE FOR THE SERIES

Feasibility of Disposal of High-Level Radioactive Waste into the Seabed

SUMMARY REPORT

Volume 1:   Overview of Research and Conclusions

TECHNICAL REPORTS

Volume 2:   Radiological Assessment

Volume 3:   Geoscience Characterisation Studies

Volume 4:   Engineering

Volume 5:   Dispersal of Radionuclides in the Oceans: Models, Data
             Sets, and Regional Descriptions

Volume 6:   Deep-Sea Biology, Biological Processes, and Radiobiology

Volume 7:   Review of Laboratory Investigations of Radionuclide
             Migration through Deep-Sea Sediments

Volume 8:   Review of Processes near a Buried Waste Canister

The summary report, which provides an overview of the research and a
summary of the results, is also available in French. The technical reports
contain detailed descriptions of the studied areas and are published in
English only.

D.R. Anderson (United States) and C.N. Murray (Commission of the
European Communities) played major roles in the Seabed Working Group. Their
work as a team to provide overall managerial direction and coordination is
acknowledged.

Also acknowledged is K.R. Hinga, the Series Editor, for his excellent
contribution to the organisation and presentation of the reports.

#19808589. me

ORDER FORM

SPECIAL 30 % DISCOUNT

Use this order form to receive a 30 % discount when you purchase the entire set of the 8 volume series "Feasibility of Disposal of High-Level Radioactive Waste into the Seabed", published by the OECD Nuclear Energy Agency.

Please enter my order for ....set(s) at the special 30 % discounted price of
FF994 £116.00 US$219 DM427

The volumes may also be purchased individually

. . . . copy(ies) Volume 1 – OVERVIEW OF RESEARCH AND CONCLUSIONS
(66 88 09 1) ISBN 92-64-13164-7 FF90 US$20.00 £11.00 DM39

. . . . copy(ies) Volume 2 – RADIOLOGICAL ASSESSMENT
(66 88 10 1) ISBN 92-64-13165-5 FF220 US$48.50 £26.00 DM95

ACTERIZATION STUDIES
-64-13166-3 FF220 US$48.50 £26.00 DM95

-64-13167-1 FF170 US$37.50 £20.00 DM74

ONUCLIDES IN THE OCEANS: MODELS, DATA
L DESCRIPTIONS
-64-13168-X ' FF280 US$62.00 £33.00 DM121

GY, RADIOLOGICAL PROCESSES AND

64-13169-8 FF150 US$33.00 £18.00 DM65

ATORY INVESTIGATIONS OF RADIONUCLIDES
GH DEEP-SEA SEDIMENTS
64-13170-1 FF190 US$42.00 £22.50 DM82

ES NEAR A BURIED WASTE CANISTER
64-13171-X FF100 US$22.00 £12.00 DM43

US$.......... DM..........

rder. Libraries must attach a purchase order to

d the French franc price).

Signature

Send this order form to : **OECD Publications Service, 2 rue André-Pascal, 75775 Paris CEDEX 16, France.** You may also order through one of the OECD Publications distributors listed on the inside back cover of this book, in which case you will be billed in local currency in keeping with usual practices.

FEASIBILITY OF DISPOSAL OF HIGH-LEVEL RADIOACTIVE WASTE INTO THE SEABED

VOLUME 8

REVIEW OF PROCESSES NEAR A BURIED WASTE CANISTER

BY
F. LANZA

NUCLEAR ENERGY AGENCY
ORGANISATION FOR ECONOMIC CO-OPERATION AND DEVELOPMENT

Pursuant to article 1 of the Convention signed in Paris on 14th December, 1960, and which came into force on 30th September, 1961, the Organisation for Economic Co-operation and Development (OECD) shall promote policies designed:

- to achieve the highest sustainable economic growth and employment and a rising standard of living in Member countries, while maintaining financial stability, and thus to contribute to the development of the world economy;
- to contribute to sound economic expansion in Member as well as non-member countries in the process of economic development; and
- to contribute to the expansion of world trade on a multilateral, non-discriminatory basis in accordance with international obligations.

The original Member countries of the OECD are Austria, Belgium, Canada, Denmark, France, the Federal Republic of Germany, Greece, Iceland, Ireland, Italy, Luxembourg, the Netherlands, Norway, Portugal, Spain, Sweden, Switzerland, Turkey, the United Kingdom and the United States. The following countries became Members subsequently through accession at the dates indicated hereafter: Japan (28th April, 1964), Finland (28th January, 1969), Australia (7th June, 1971) and New Zealand (29th May, 1973).

The Socialist Federal Republic of Yugoslavia takes part in some of the work of the OECD (agreement of 28th October, 1961).

The OECD Nuclear Energy Agency (NEA) was established in 1957 under the name of the OEEC European Nuclear Energy Agency. It received its present designation on 20th April, 1972, when Japan became its first non-European full Member. NEA membership today consists of all European Member countries of OECD as well as Australia, Canada, Japan and the United States. The commission of the European Communities takes part in the work of the Agency.

The primary objective of NEA is to promote co-operation between the governments of its participating countries in furthering the development of nuclear power as a safe, environmentally acceptable and economic energy source.

This is achieved by:

- *encouraging harmonisation of national, regulatory policies and practices, with particular reference to the safety of nuclear installations, protection of man against ionising radiation and preservation of the environment, radioactive waste management, and nuclear third party liability and insurance;*
- *assessing the contribution of nuclear power to the overall energy supply by keeping under review the technical and economic aspects of nuclear power growth and forecasting demand and supply for the different phases of the nuclear fuel cycle;*
- *developing exchanges of scientific and technical information particularly through participation in common services;*
- *setting up international research and development programmes and joint undertakings.*

In these and related tasks, NEA works in close collaboration with the International Atomic Energy Agency in Vienna, with which it has concluded a Co-operation Agreement, as well as with other international organisations in the nuclear field.

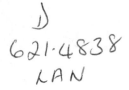

621·4838
LAN

SUMMARY

The scope of the NFTG was to investigate the phenomena arriving in the proximity of the waste package immersed in the sea sediments.

A first consequence of the presence of the waste package particularly when it contains high level waste of recent origin is to generate a thermal field in the sediments.

As a consequence a thermosyphon driven motion of the pore water is possible. Predictions suggest that for a red clay sea sedimens the induced pore water would move on the order of one meter in one thousand years.

The analysis was continued to see if in such a condition the canister will move. Calculations were performed with two different computer codes. It appears that with the most pessimistic assumptions the maximum displacement is around 40 cm. As it is assumed usually that the canister will be at a depth of 30-40 meters this effect can be considered negligible.

The assumptions made on the required characteristics of canister materials have been largely discussed. Proposals range from the minimum required to contain the conditioned waste until burial, to containers designed to keep their integrity as long as 500 years. The longer lifetime is defined by the desire of an additional barrier during the period in which cesium-17 and strontium-90 are present and heat generation keeps the package at a temperature significantly higher than the sediments.

Two different canister concepts are being considered to achieve the multiple hundred year life expectancy. The first utilizes a very corrosion-resistant material in a relatively thin canister or overpacking (e.g. titanium-based alloy). The second one is based on a relatively inexpensive metal which could be used economically in a thick section to make allowance for corrosion losses (mild steel).

A large number of tests have been devoted to evaluate the candidates materials for both options.

Titanium base alloys, and in particular Ticode 12 alloy, have been considered mainly for high temperature applications. High resistance to general attack up to 250°C has been shown, with average dissolution rates not exceeding 0,012 mm/yr.

Bearing in mind that passive corrosion normally exhibits parabolic rather than linear kinetics, this rate, derived from short term tests - should be pessimistic. Titanium and its alloys may be subject to hydrogen embrittlement. This is most likely to occur under reducing conditions, but could also occur under oxidizing conditions due to radiolytically generated hydrogen. Hydrogen pick-up will be accelerated by high disposal temperatures, but cracking is unlikely to occur until the canisters have cooled below 100°C. The titanium alloys under consideration for waste canisters are generally resistant to stress corrosion cracking. However, no information is available on their long-term behaviour at high disposal temperatures.

At moderate temperatures (i.e. up to 100°C) the general corrosion of carbon steel is normally controlled by the rate of transport of oxygen and other oxidizing species. However, in the case of waste containers the rate of oxygen diffusion is so low that corrosion by direct reaction with water is dominant. Laboratory tests in deaerated seawater under inactive conditions have indicated a corrosion rate of the order of 0.008 mm/yr at 90°C. Tests performed in sea sediments have shown higher corrosion value, particularly when the sediments are rich in carbonates. Tests of longer duration are needed to control whether the value obtained corresponds really to the steady state. It has to be noted, however, that if the decrease of the temperature at the interface with the time is taken into account, even such a high value can be considered acceptable.

Carbon steel canisters are unlikely to be subject to significant pitting corrosion under the low oxygen conditions anticipated in marine sediments. It is unlikely that the carbon steel canisters will be subject to stress corrosion cracking. One possible area of susceptibility is the hard metallurgical structures produced in sealing welds. These should be avoided by using steels with an appropriately low carbon equivalent or by heat treating the canisters after sealing.

As underlined in the general introduction we will consider that the container will last for the so-called thermal period, so that when the glass, after the dissolution or the desintegration of the container, will come in contact with the sea sedments, no thermal gradient will be present. Apart from this, the gamma activity will be reduced to a negligible level. The main activity present will be the soft beta due to the long life fission products and the alpha emitted by the actinides.

As a consequence, the leaching of the glass will arrive in isothermal conditions at a temperature probably slightly higher than that of the indisturbed condition (2°C) and radiation effect will be limited to the damage to the glass due to alpha radiation and to the recoil of the alpha emitters.

Due to the fact that the leaching rate at 2°C is rather low tests have been performed at higher temperatures. Extrapolation at the sediment temperature is performed assuming an Arrhenius relationship. A limited amount of tests in sea water and sea sediments have been performed. The conclusions must then be considered only preliminary.

Static tests conducted in sea water have shown that after an initial period of fast linear corrosion, the attack slows down noticeably. It seems probable that in this second period the glass leaching depends on a silica concentration which is controlled by the reprecipitation of an aluminio-magnesium silicate.

Tests in sediments for the period investigated show only the linear part. It appears that the absorptive properties of the sediments do not allow to reach such a concentration of silica which gives rise to saturation effects.

It seems probable that for longer times, when the absorptive sites are saturated, even on sediments, lower leaching rates will be encountered. However, lacking the experimental evidence, it seems advisable to be conservative and assume that even for long periods of time the degradation rate continues to be linear.

The release of the less soluble elements is controlled by a diffusion mechanism and, after an initial period, is independent from the glass degradation rate.

The influence of the radiation damage of the glass, of the radiolysis of the interstitial sea water, of the water pressure does not appear to be large. Probably the effect of all these phenomena does not go beyond the degree of the uncertainty of the data assumed.

When the canister is immersed in the sediment the temperature will increase due to the heat released by the fission product. In particular the sediment in the near field will reach the highest temperature. In the assumption of the burial of fresh radioactive waste maximum temperature would reach 300°C. Moreover due to the presence of a heat flux a large thermal gradient will be present.

A study has been conducted to on different types of sediment to analyse the interaction of the sediments with the sea water and to investigate the influence on the thermal gradient on the mobility of the sea water constituents.

CONTENTS

CHAPTER 1: INTRODUCTION

A waste package emplaced in the subseabed is completely immersed in sediment. The region of sediment surrounding the waste package is known as the near field region. The definition of this term as it applies to land-based repositories relies mainly on a distinction between engineered structures and geological environments. With respect to subseabed disposal, near field is defined by distinguishing between sediments that are and are not in their natural condition. The near field in a subseabed repository would comprise those sediments that were altered by high temperatures, radiation fields, adsorption of corrosion products, or sediments which are not in isothermal, or near-istothermal conditions ("near isothermal" describes a situation in which the diffusion driven by the concentration gradient). Such a region is delimited by two boundaries. The waste package, which acts as a source term, is the inner boundary of the near field. The waste package is the source of either corrosion products or the various species released by the degraded glass. The external boundary is sediment in its natural conditions, or far field sediment. At its external boundary, the near field acts as a source term for the far field.

A large number of phenomena such as corrosion, leaching, complexing, and reprecipitation of various chemical species, diffusion, and adsorption can occur in the near field. Besides during the initial phase of the repository life, the heat generation of the canister can induce thermosyphon pore water movement which could change drastically the transport of the released radionuclides. Study of the near field can be simplified, however, by assuming that the metallic canister will protect the waste form while the temperature increase and temperature gradient in the near field are significant. As a first approximation for the canister a life of at least 500 years can be considered necessary. Making this assumption implies that for the normal operating condition the thermal gradients, the corresponding thermal diffusion and pore water movement and radiolysis will affect only canister corrosion. On the contrary, in the case of an accidental condition, these phenomena will influence also the release of radionuclides. It appeared reasonable to study firstly the normal operating conditions, leaving for a succesive period the study of the conditions corresponding to the various possible accidents.

The near field will be discussed by division into the following topics:

1) Thermal fileds and induced pore water movement.
2) Canister motion studies.
3) Canister corrosion.
4) Waste form leaching.
5) Sea water-sediment interaction.

It has to be noted that in the study of the near field the age of the waste immobilised in the glass plays an important role. In fact, from this parameter depends the amount of heat released by the canister and as a consequence the temperature at the interface between the canister (or the overcoating) and the sediments. Two options were utilized during the study. The first one, mainly utilized in the U.S. studies, assumes a waste 10 years old. The second, mainly utilized in the European studies, assumes a waste at least 50 years old.

Due to budgettary difficulties american scientists were not able to participate to the final redaction of this report.

In the preparation of this final report a large use has been made of the following reports:
- J.A.C. Marples - Factors affecting the leachability of vitrified waste - S.P. 1.07.C2.85.50;
- G.P. Marsh - Factors affecting the leachability of vitrified waste - S.P. 1.07.C2.85.50;

- W.E. Seyfried, Jr and E.C. Thornton - Sea water-sediment interaction at elevated temperature and pressure and in response to a thermal gradient - S.P. 1.07.C2.85.52;

of the series: "Study of the feasibility and safety of the disposal of heat generating wastes in deep oceanic geological formations edited C.N. MURRAY.

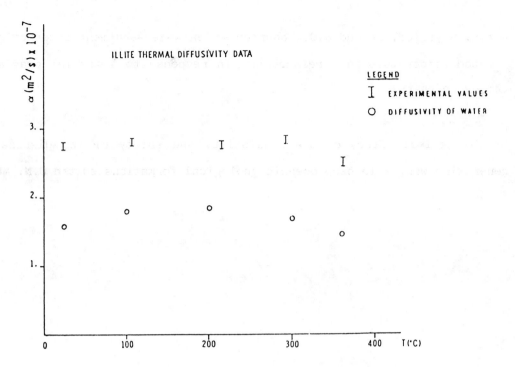

FIGURE 2.1.   Illite thermal diffusivity data.

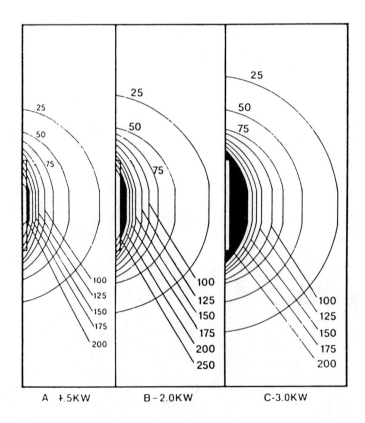

FIGURE 2.2.   Isotherm plots showing maximum penetration of 200°C
isotherm into sediment.

CHAPTER 2:   THERMAL FIELDS AND INDUCED PORE WATER MOVEMENT

Heat can move through a medium by one of, or a combination of, three processes: conduction, convection and radiation. Thermal studies, including both
transport model development and laboratory testing, indicate that for sediment
made up of clay sized particles the thermal energy will be transported from the
waste package through the sediments to the infinite heat sink of the approximately 2°C ocean waters by thermal conduction. The sediment from the more geologically stable oceanographic areas of interest to the program in both the
Atlantic and Pacific are made up of approximately the same particle size and
bulk permeability as the red clays which have been tested.

In order to put into evidence the maximum possible effects, the study has
been conducted in the assumption of a 10 year old waste.

2.1 Model Development

To date two thermal transport models have been developed: Coyaote /1/ and
Mariah /2/. Sensitivity analyses of the input parameters for those models have
shown that the thermal conductivity was the only parameter to have an important
effect on the thermal transport. The thermal conductivity of samples of the red
clay sediments was then measured at 500 bar pressure over a range of temperature from 20°C to 400°C. As can be seen in Figure 2.1, the laboratory measured
thermal diffusivity (1/thermal conductivity) was essentially constant over the
temperature range of interest and thus will not introduce any large errors into
the thermal field calculations. A final in-situ proof of the conductivity measurement will be needed, however.

Thermal environment predictions, Figure 2.2, show that for the 10 years
old high-level waste the 100°C isotherm would have a radius of approximately

0.5 m for a 1.5 kWatt (1.5 metric ton of heavy metal) and 0.8 m radius for a 2.0 kWatt (2.0 metric ton of heavy metal) source.

2.2 Verification

In December 1981 a large-scale (1 m^3 of reconsolidated sediment), in-situ conditions (530 bar pressure and 4°C) laboratory test of the Mariah code was initiated. Preliminary results indicate that the heat did move through the sediments by conduction and that Mariah did predict the measured thermal field.

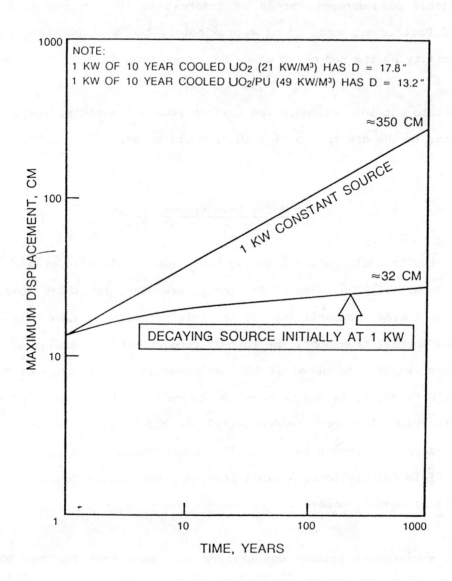

FIGURE 2.3

An in-situ, deep sea, field test of the thermal model will be conducted during the In-Situ Heat Transfer Experiment (ISHTE) to be fielded around 1986. This experiment will be a 1 year test using a scaled heater (400 Watts) in the surface sediments at a site of interest to the international program.

Ion transport models are sensitive to any advection of the pore water. Results from the aforementioned models and small laboratory tests were used to estimate how much induced pore water movement might be expected from a 10 kWatt canister of 10 year old high-level waste. Predictions suggest that for the red clay mentioned above the induced pore water would move on the order of one metre in one thousand years, see Figure 2.3.

2.3 Engineering Trade-Off Studies

Using both of the mathematical models discussed above, a simplified version developed especially for the trade-off studies, the following conclusions have been drawn:

- a 10% decrease in sediment conductivity would decrease the loading of HLW waste in the canister by 9%;

- a 10% decrease in sediment heat capacity would decrease the loading of HLW in the canister by 1%;

- a 10% decrease in the sediment porosity decreases the conductivity by 6% thus the loading of HLW by 5%;

- the depth of burial has no effect on canister temperature beyond burial depths of 4 m;

- for a maximum temperature at the canister surface the horinzontal spacing is insensitive to distances greater than 11 m;

- the temperatures around a can are a linear function of the amount of high-level waste placed in the canister;

- ageing the waste an additional 5 years allows an increase of 30% in the loading of radionuclides within the canister;

- the temperature around a canister for any loading is proportional to the radius$^{1.7}$;

- the temperature field (horizontal plane, canister midline) around a canister is insensitive to canister lengths greater than 18 m;

- the temperature field (horizontal plane, canister midline) around a canister is insensitive to canisters spaced greater than 7 m in a vertical line (drilled emplacement);

- the temperature field (horizontal plane, canister midline) around a canister is insensitive to more than six canisters in a vertical line (drilled emplacement).

References

/1/ Gartling, D.K. (1978). COYOTE - A finite element computer program for non-linear heat conduction problems. SAND77-1332, Sandia Laboratories, Albuquerque, NM, June 1978.

/2/ Gartling, D.K., MARIAH - A finite element computer program for incompressible porous flow problems. Part I: Theoretical background, SAND79-1622, Part II: Users manual, SAND79-1623, Sandia Laboratories, Albuquerque, NM (in preparation).

/3/ Percival, M.C. (1982). Laboratory simulation of a deep ocean in-situ heat transfer experiment. SAND82-1553, IEEE/IATA Conf., September 20-22, Washington, D.C.

/4/ Klett, R.D. (1981). Initial phase of the subseabed thermal sensitivity studies. in K.R. Hinga ed., Subseabed Disposal Program Annual Report, January to December 1980, Vol. II, SAND81-1095/11, Sandia National Laboratories, Albuquerque, NM, July 1981.

CHAPTER 3: CANISTER MOTION STUDIES

Coupled thermal and mechanical loading of the marine sediment in the vicinity of an emplaced, high-density, heat-producing waste canister has the potential of inducing canister motion in the sediment column. Due to the low in-situ heating rate, such induced motion will occur over a relatively long time scale (i.e. tens of years), and we, therefore, characterise it as creeping motion to distinguish it from the more rapid sediment motion associated with emplacement activities. Developing a capability to predict the long-term movement of a canister, along with the sediment and pore around it, is one of the essential steps in testing feasibility of the concept.

Generally speaking, subsequent movement of an emplaced waste canister is the result of a complex interaction of buoyancy effects (i.e. sediment and pore water near the canister are warmer and thus less dense than they are further away) and temperature-induced changes in the strength of the sediment. In particular it is necessary to account explicitly for the relative motions of canister, sediment and pore water.

Two elements are essential to obtain a realistic prediction of the long-term coupled thermomechanical interactions that occur between an emplaced waste canister and marine sediment. These are:

1) a suitable computer code to perform calculations involving large deformations over long time scales;
2) a material model for the sediment which is consistent with laboratory data defining the effects of environmental factors on time-dependent deformation. In this context, the relevant environmental factors include stress and temperature.

Initial calculations of canister motion were done using a relatively simple material model and computer code /1/. For the material model, it was assumed that the sediment behaves as a non-linear viscous solid with a temperature-dependent viscosity. A computer code, COUPLEFLD, developed to analyse creeping viscous flow of solids was used for these initial calculations.

Sensitivity calculations demonstrate how various parameters in the problem affect the solution. The parameters that were varied included initial heat load of the canister, canister density and sediment viscosity. Results for canister motion due to variations in these parameters are given in Figures 3.1, 3.2 and 3.3 respectively. Sediment motion was also calculated, and an example of these results is given in Figure 3.4. Although all the results obtained in this study suggest that very little thermomechanically coupled motion occurs, this conclusion must be tempered by taking note of the simplifications that were utilized in these calculations.

A new computer code, NEPTUNE, was developed in an effort to reduce the limitations inherent in COUPLEFLO. The principal advantage of NEPTUNE is that it is capable of accounting for the relative motion of the sediment skeleton (assumed to be a porous, viscous solid) and the interstitial pore water in the sediment. The material constants used in initial NEPTUNE calculations are summarized in Table 3.1. For these calculations, the waste canister was assumed to be spherical and the parameter variations that were done are given in Table 3.2, with the corresponding peak canister velocities given in Table 3.3. Representative results for canister, sediment, and pore water motion histories are given in Figures 3.5, 3.6 and 3.7.

The general conclusion one can draw when comparing COUPLEFLO and NEPTUNE results for canister motion predictions is that the motion is substantially reduced when NEPTUNE is used. The reason for this reduced motion is that the flow of pore water calculated in NEPTUNE results in an energy dissipation which is not present in the more restricted COUPLEFLO solution. Review of Table 3.2 and 3.3 clearly shows, however, that canister motion is dependent on the material model assumed. The next stage in obtaining a realistic prediction of canister motion is thus to refine the material model based on the results of recent laboratory studies.

References

/1/ Chavez, P.F. and Dawson, P.R. (1981). Thermally induced motion of marine sediments resulting from disposal of radioactive waste. Sandia National Laboratories Report SAND80-1476, January 1981.

TABLE 3.1. MATERIAL PROPERTIES.

	Skeleton	Pore fluid	Canister	
Density	2800	1000	4000	(kg/m^3)
Heat capacity	800	4500	864	(W/k K)
Conductivity	1.92	0.625	1.25	$(W/m^2 K)$
Expensivity	$5.0x10^{-4}$	(*)	0.0	(1/k)

Porosity = 0.8

Drag coefficient, b = $1x10^{12}$ and $1x10^{13}$ (Pa s/m^2)

Skeleton viscosities: $\mu = 0.17x10^{-7} e^{14700/\theta}$ (Pa s)

$\kappa = 10^{20}$ and 10^{21} (Pa s)

(*) α_{exp} = $2.5x10^{-4}$ + $4.4x10^{-6}$ (-273)

TABLE 3.2. HEATING SPHERE SIMULATIONS.

Case	Canister density (kg/m^3)	Viscosity (k) (Pa s)	Drag coefficient (b) (Pa s/m^2)
A	2280	10^{20}	10^{13}
B	4000	10^{20}	10^{13}
C	2280	10^{21}	10^{12}
D	2280	10^{20}	10^{12}
E	4000	10^{21}	10^{12}
F	4000	10^{20}	10^{12}

TABLE 3.3. PEAK CANISTER VELOCITY.

Case	Peak canister velocity (pm/s)
A	- 5.8
B	-27.5
C	- 1.59
D	- 5.8
E	- 9.5
F	-27.3

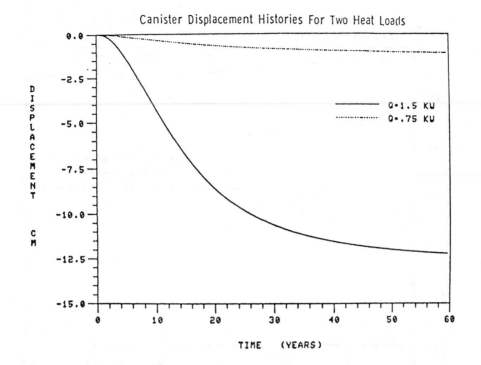

FIGURE 3.1. Canister displacement histories for two heat loads.

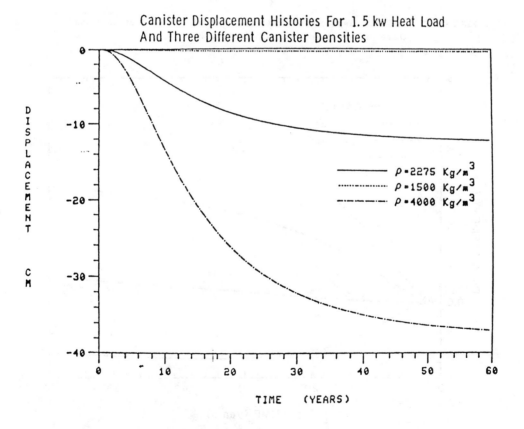

FIGURE 3.2. Canister displacement histories for 1.5 kW heat load and three
different canister densities.

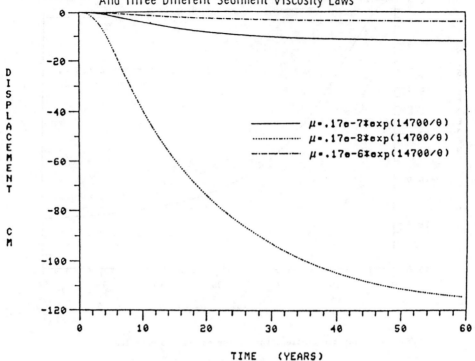

FIGURE 3.3. Canister displacement histories assuming 1.5 kW heat load and
three different sediment viscosity laws.

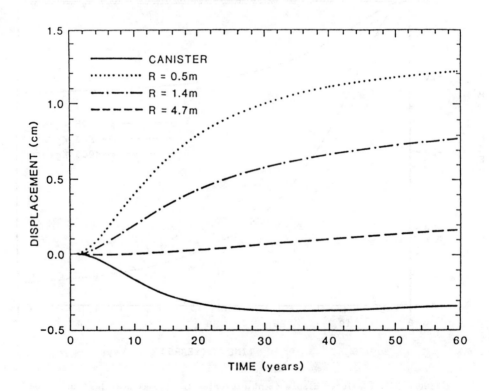

FIGURE 3.4. Sediment motion for differents canister radius.

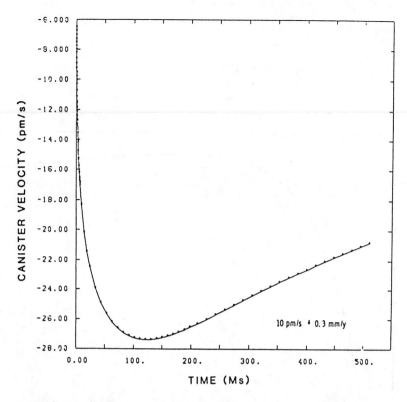

FIGURE 3.5. Canister velocity as a function of time.

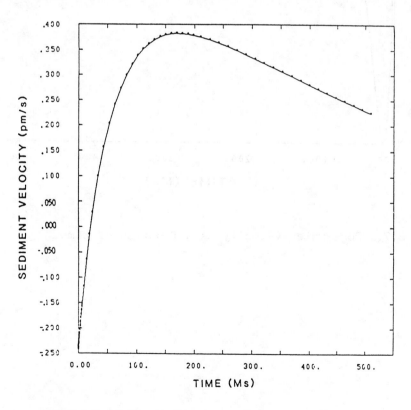

FIGURE 3.6. Sediment velocity as a function of time.

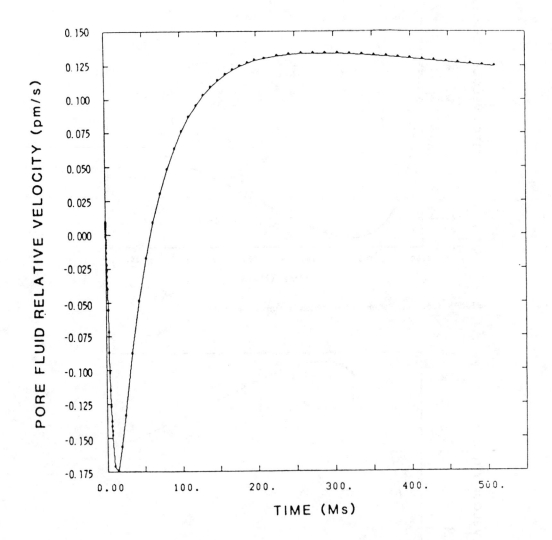

FIGURE 3.7. Pore water velocity as a function of time.

CHAPTER 4: CANISTER CORROSION

4.1 Introduction

The assumptions made on the required characteristics of canister materials have been largely discussed. Proposals range from the minimum required to contain the conditioned waste until burial, to containers designed to keep their integrity as long as 500 years. The longer lifetime is defined by the desire of an additional barrier during the period in which cesium-137 and strontium-90 are present and heat generation keeps the package at a temperature significantly higher than the sediments.

As indicated in the introduction, the possibility of having an additional barrier during the heat generating period gives many advantages. We will consider as a goal the development of a container which could withstand 500 years in the sediments.

Two different canister concepts are being considered to achieve the multiple hundred year life expectancy /1/. The first utilizes a very corrosion-resistant material in a relatively thin canister or overpacking (e.g. titanium-based alloy). The second one is based on a relatively inexpensive metal which could be used economically in a thick section to make allowance for corrosion losses (mild steel). Highly resistant corrosion materials have been studied in connection with the assumption of the disposal of a recent waste. A maximum interface temperature of 250°C has been taken into consideration. Corrosion allowance materials ask for thick containers. The interface temperature then can be considered depending not only on the age of the radioactive waste but also on the thickness of the container and, more in general, from its design. A maximum interface temperature of 100°C has been assumed.

This chapter considers the effects of temperature and pressure on the performance of both the corrosion-resistant and corrosion allowance canisters. This is done by giving a brief description of the corrosion characteristics of the metals covering the various types of attack to which they may be susceptible. Consideration is then given to how the form of corrosion (e.g. general, pitting, crevice, stress corrosion, etc.) may vary depending on the environmental conditions, and where possible data on the rates of attack are included. Since the behaviour of the corrosion-resistant and corrosion allowance canister metals is quite different they are discussed separately.

4.2 Corrosion-Resistant Metals

Titanium and its alloys normally exhibit excellent resistance to general corrosion in neutral aqueous environments. This good behaviour, from a metal which thermodynamically is very active, is attributable to the formation of a thin but extremely protective surface layer of TiO_2. Figure 4.1 shows a potential pH diagram, which indicates the thermodynamic equilibria for titanium in water at 25°C. This shows that in principle TiO_2 should be produced by the reaction of titanium with water alone, at near neutral pH levels.

Electrochemically the reaction involves the following steps:

$$Ti + 2 H_2O \rightarrow TiO_2 + 4 H^+ + 4 e \quad \text{(anodic)} \tag{4.1}$$

$$4 H^+ + 4 e \rightarrow 2 H_2 \quad \text{(cathodic)} \tag{4.2}$$

$$Ti + 2 H_2O \rightarrow TiO_2 + 2 H_2 \quad \text{(overall)} \tag{4.3}$$

However, the cathodic reaction (2) is extremely sluggish on pure titanium surfaces /2,3/, and therefore it is doubtful whether this alone will be able to sustain the TiO_2 surface film. Although not proved unequivocally it is likely that a small concentration of oxygen will also be needed /4/.

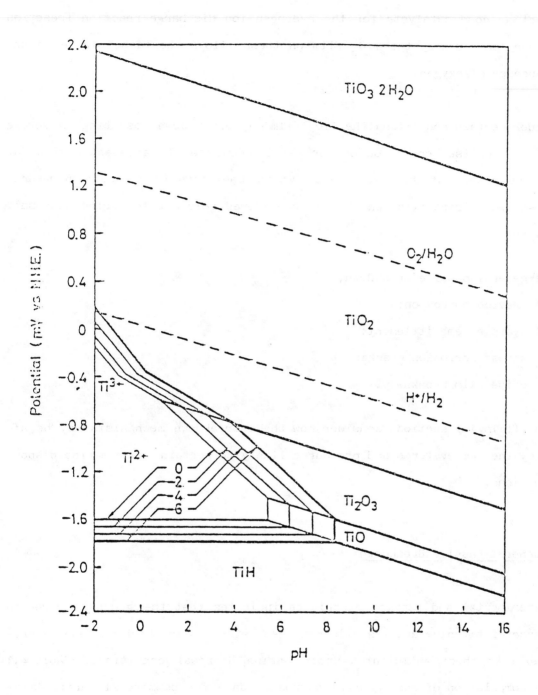

FIGURE 4.1. Potential pH diagram for titanium in water at 25°C.

In contrast to the behaviour observed with pure titanium, reaction (2) occurs at a much faster rate on the surfaces of the Ti-0.2%Pd and Ti-0.8%Ni-0.3%Mo alloys. This is because both alloys contain intermetallic precipitates chich act as good catalysts for the hydrogen ion discharge reaction (reaction (2)). As a consequence, the TiO_2 film on these alloys should be stable in the total absence of oxygen.

Under certain conditions the TiO_2 film may break down resulting in severe general or localised corrosion of the metal substrate. In a recent review /4/ on the behaviour of titanium based waste canisters, five such breakdown mechanisms were identified, which were considered relevant to marine disposal. These were:

    a) general passive breakdown;

    b) crevice corrosion;

    c) hydrogen embrittlement;

    d) stress corrosion cracking;

    e) oxide film breakaway.

The following sections consider how these breakdown mechanisms may be affected by the temperatures and pressures likely to pertain under marine disposal conditions.

4.2.1 General Passive Breakdown

Experimental and service experience indicates that the general corrosion resistance of titanium and its alloys in sea water remains high at temperatures comparable to those anticipated under marine disposal conditions. Table 4.1 gives a compilation of such general corrosion data for commercial purity titanium, and it is significant that even at 250°C the reported wastage rates do not exceed 11.7 μ/yr. Bearing in mind that passive corrosion normally exhibits

TABLE 4.1. GENERAL CORROSION RATES FOR COMMERCIAL PURITY TITANIUM IN SEA WATER
            OR 3.5% NaCl SOLUTION.

Temperature (°C)	Pressure (MPa)	Exposure time (days)	Corrosion rate (µm/yr)	Reference
Ambient	–		2.0	5
Ambient	–	1643	7.4×10^{-4}	6
Ambient	7.2–20.6	123–1064	2.5	7
60	–	146	0.24	8
130	–	146	1.6	8
200	–	146	3.2	8
250	4.0	30	11.7	9

parabolic rather than linear kinetics, these rates - derived from short-term
tests - should be pessimistic.

The results in Table 4.1 also suggest that the stability of the pas-
sivating TiO_2 surface layer is not adversely affected by pressure. It should be
stressed, however, that the data only cover pressures up to 4.0 MPa, whereas
the pressures anticipated in marine disposal may be as great as 70 MPa. In
principle, hydrostatic pressure will displace the thermodynamic equilibrium of
the $Ti-TiO_2$ reaction (i.e. reaction (1)) because of the volume change involved.
However, this effect (i.e. P V) is only equivalent to 0.170 Kcals which is very
small compared to the reaction energy of 196.3 Kcals (at 25°C).

Overall, existing experience suggests that the general corrosion resistance of titanium based waste canisters should not be impaired by the temperatures and pressures anticipated under marine disposal conditions. However, this
experience is based on experimental and plant service periods which are short
in comparison to the life times required from the canisters. The longer term
corrosion resistance of the canisters will depend on the environment remaining
sufficiently oxidizing to stabilize the TiO_2 surface film. It will also depend
on the TiO_2 layer retaining its protective properties and not being subject to

the "breakaway" phenomenon sometimes observed with titanium under stongly
oxidizing conditions. This is discussed in a later section (Section 4.2.5).

Another point which should be emphasized is that pressure is not the only
important factor which will vary depending on the disposal depth. In particular, it is known that the oxygen level in both sea water and marine sediments
varies with depth, and as stated previously, this may be important in determining the stability of the protective TiO_2 film on canisters fabricated from commercial purity titanium.

4.2.2 Crevice Corrosion

Local breakdown of the TiO_2 passive film leading to severe corrosion may
occur in crevices where, because of restricted transport, the solution chemistry becomes much more aggressive (i.e. increased acidity, chloride concentration) than that of the bulk environment. Susceptibility to crevice corrosion
increases with temperature and chloride concentration as illustrated for commercial purity titanium and the Ti-0.2%Pd alloy in Figures 4.2 and 4.3. Equivalent data are not available for the Ti-0.8%Ni-0.3%Mo alloy, but work in the USA
indicates that this should behave in a similar manner to the Ti-0.2%Pd alloy.
From the comparative viewpoint it is significant that, in sea water, crevice
corrosion can occur with commercial purity titanium at temperatures exceeding
130°C, but that the Ti-0.2%Pd alloy is resistant up to 170°C.

In practice, the occurrence of crevice corrosion depends on, amongst other
factors, the redox potential of the environment and the geometry and nature of
the crevice. For example, long tight crevices are more likely to promote corrosion than short open crevices, and the risk of crevice initiation falls with
the redox (oxidizing) potential of the environment. In marine disposal one in-
evitable crevice is that formed between the canister and the sediment, however,

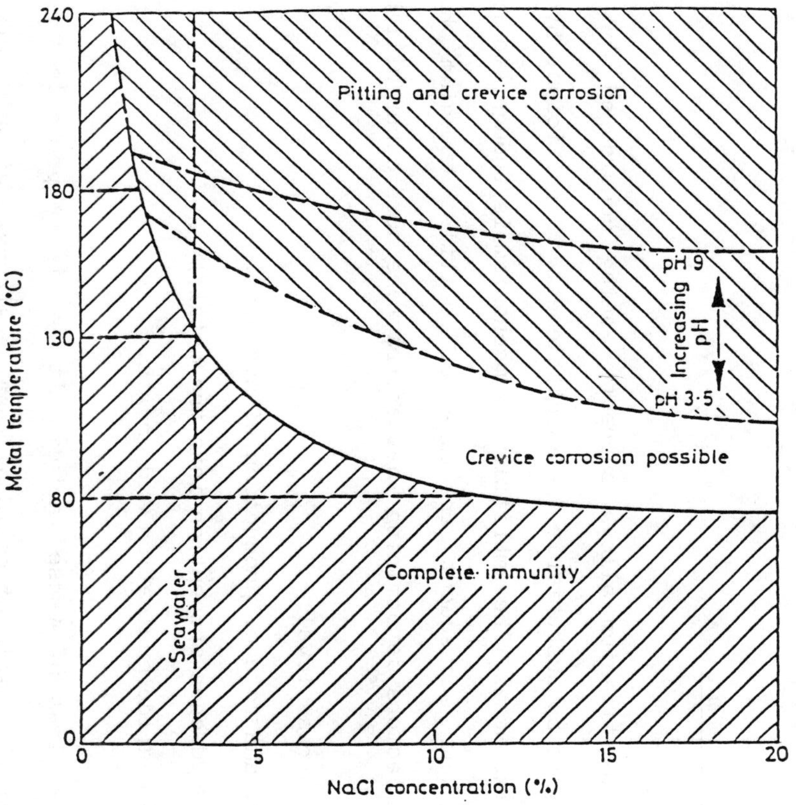

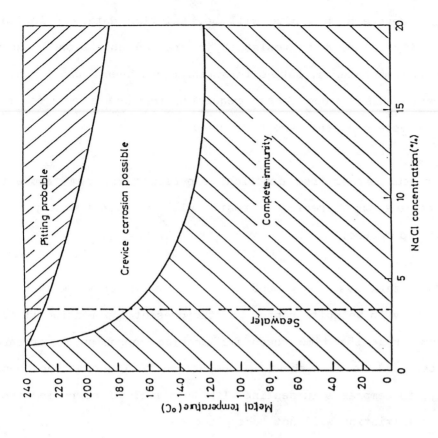

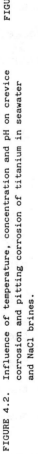

FIGURE 4.2. Influence of temperature, concentration and pH on crevice corrosion and pitting corrosion of titanium in seawater and NaCl brines.

FIGURE 4.3. Influence of temperature and concentration on crevice corrosion and pitting corrosion propensity of titanium alloy 260 (Ti-0.45% Pd) in sea water and NaCl brines.

it is not clear how severe such a site will be. Existing data /9/ indicates that commercial purity titanium is resistant to crevice corrosion in seabed sediments at ambient temperatures, but no information has been found for higher temperatures. Clearly this is one factor requiring further investigation if corrosion-resistant waste canisters are to be used.

There is no reason either from practical experience or from theoretical understanding to believe that crevice corrosion will be significantly influenced by hydrostatic pressure.

No quantitative data has been found on the rate of crevice corrosion, although this is likely to be quite rapid. For the present application it seems reasonable to assume that the time taken for crevice corrosion to propagate through the canister will be very short in comparison to the canisters design life. Consequently, the emphasis in dealing with this form of corrosion should be on assuring that initiation will not take place.

4.2.3 Hydrogen Embrittlement

All three of the titanium alloys currently being considered for waste canisters are likely to be susceptible to embrittlement if sufficient hydrogen is introduced into the metal. The embrittlement mechanism is thought to involve the precipitation and subsequent fracture of brittle titanium hydride platelets. The main factors determining whether fracture does occur will be:

a) the tensile stress level;
b) the activity and rate of production of hydrogen;
c) the rate of hydrogen absorption into the metal;
d) the rate of hydride nucleation and growth.

Considering the first of these factors, it is highly probable that the canisters will contain significant residual tensile stresses after fabrication.

It is not clear, however, how these stresses will be modified by the high hydrostatic pressures imposed by marine disposal. If this pressure is sufficient to cancel out the tensile stresses or even subject the canisters to purely compressive loading, this would avoid the risk of hydrogen embrittlement fracture. It is recommended that the engineering studies currently underway on canister design and emplacement should include stress analyses to cover this point.

Turning to the second of the above factors it is likely that two sources of hydrogen will be operative under disposal conditions. These will involve the electrochemical generation of hydrogen (i.e. reaction (2)), and hydrogen production by the radiolytic breakdown of water. The first of these will accelerate with increasing temperature, but no information has been found on the effect of temperature on the radiolytic yield. Limited information indicates that the rate of the electrochemical reaction is not affected by pressure /11/, but once again the response of the radiolytic process is not clear. It is possible that the hydrostatic pressure will increase the activity of hydrogen at the canister surface simply by increasing the solubility of the gas. The magnitude of this effect is unclear, however, because the hydrogen will be free to diffuse away from the canister.

The rate of absorption of hydrogen by titanium is controlled by diffusion through the TiO_2 surface film, because this is much less permeable to hydrogen than the metal itself. The diffusion coefficient for hydrogen in TiO_2 varies with temperature according to the expressions /12/:

$$Da = 2.7 \times 10^{-6} \exp(-13100/RT) \ cm^2 sec^{-1} \tag{4.4}$$

$$Dc = 7.5 \times 10^{-6} \exp(-9040/RT) \ cm^2 sec^{-1} \tag{4.5}$$

for the a and c crystallographic directions in the tetragonal latice (i.e. for rutile). These indicate that the diffusion coefficient can increase by up to 10^4 between 20 and 250°C.

The solubility of hydrogen in titanium also increases with temperature. Consequently, the nucleation of hydrides will be favoured by low temperatures. This factor is thought to account for the reduced susceptibility to hydrogen embrittlement exhibited by titanium alloys at temperatures exceeding 100°C (Figure 4.4).

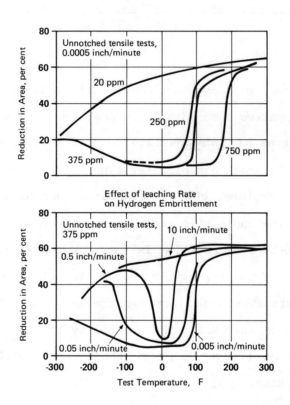

FIGURE 4.4.   Effects of hydrogen content, strain rate and temperature on the tensile ductility of a typical / titanium alloy.

To summarize it seems likely that the rate of production and adsorption of hydrogen will increase with temperature. At present it is not clear if the amount of hydrogen introduced into the metal will be sufficient to cause embrittlement. However, if it is, then it is likely that embrittlement fracture will not occur until the temperature has fallen sufficiently to facilitate hydride precipitation (i.e. down to $\leq$ 100°C).

4.2.4 Stress Corrosion Cracking

In common with hydrogen embrittlement, stress corrosion cracking only occurs in metals subject to tensile stressing. Therefore, the comments made in
the previous section on the possible effects of hydrostatic pressure on the
state of stress in waste canisters applies equally to this cracking process.

The distinction between hydrogen embrittlement and stress corrosion
cracking is less clear with titanium alloys than with many other metals. In
fact, some workers believe that stress corrosion occurs by a hydrogen
embrittlement mechanism, the hydrogen being generated electrochemically at the
metal surface and being adsorbed at sites where the TiO_2 film has been broken
by mechanical straining. On the other hand, however, it has also been proposed
that cracking occurs by an anodic dissolution process, once again sustained by
the mechanical rupture of the TiO_2 layer. This uncertainty over the stress
corrosion mechanism is important because, whilst the hydrogen embrittlement
process has an upper temperature limit, this may not be the case for a dissolution based cracking mechanism.

Although not totally immune, the titanium alloys under consideration for
waste canisters have a high resistance to stress corrosion in marine environments. For example, cracking has only been observed with commercial purity titanium in 2.5% NaCl solution when the oxygen content of the metal exceeds 0.31%
/13/, which is roughly three times the level in normal CP titanium. Furthermore, it appears to be a general rule that titanium alloys are only subject to
stress corrosion when a region of stress intensification is produced by a surface defect such as a notch or precrack. The implication is that stress corrosion is only likely to initiate under extreme loading. Therefore, it seems
probable that this does not constitute such a severe threat as hydrogen
embrittlement.

4.2.5 Oxide Film Breakaway

Under oxidizing conditions, passive metals have on occasions been found to reach a limit at which the oxide coating ceases to be protective and rapid corrosion ensues. This has been attributed to the film becoming so highly stressed that it fractures and allows rapid passage of reactants through the metal. The phenomenon has not been observed with titanium except in such oxidizing media as fuming nitric acid, and in sea water when the metal is subject to extreme anodic polarisation of the order of 6-10 Volts. However, titanium is a modern metal and the long-term growth characteristics of the titanium oxide layer are unknown, so the possibility of breakaway cannot be dismissed.

Under the moderate to low oxidizing conditions anticipated with marine disposal, it is probable that the rate of growth of TiO_2 will be slow. Nonetheless, breakaway is an obvious potential problem that needs to be considered. In particular the effect of hydrostatic pressure on the stress in the TiO_2 layer and its consequent effect on the possibility of breakaway merits attention.

4.3 Corrosion Allowance Metals

The potential-Ph diagram indicating the thermodynamic equilibria for iron in water at 25°C is shown in Figure 4.5. This indicates that in the pH range normally associated with sea water, iron should be protected by a layer of Fe_3O_4 or $Fe(OH)_2$. In practice, however, the high chloride ion content of sea water prevents the establishment of a completely protective layer, and steel corrodes by the general reaction:

$$Fe + nH_2O \rightarrow Fe(OH)_n^{(2-n)+} + nH^+ + 2e^- \qquad (4.6)$$

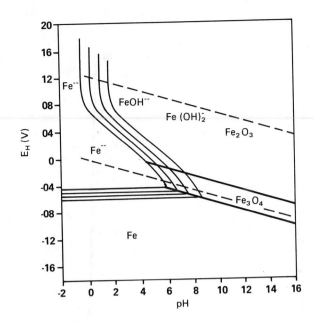

FIGURE 4.5. Potential-pH equilibrium diagram for the system iron-water at 25°C.

If this anodic reaction is to proceed it must be balanced by a cathodic reaction. Two such reactions commonly occur in aqueous environments over the relevant pH range:

$$H_2O + 0.5\ O_2 + 2e^- \rightarrow 2OH^- \tag{4.7}$$

$$2H_2O + 2e^- \rightarrow H_2 + 2OH^- \tag{4.8}$$

The rate of corrosion is usually determined by the rate of the cathodic reaction, and since the water reduction reaction (8) is comparatively slow, this normally means that the rate of attack is controlled by the transport of oxygen to the metal surface. Thus, in aerated open sea water, where the rate of transport of oxygen is high, corrosion rates are of the order of 1-10 mm/yr at 90°C /10/. By comparison corrosion rates in deaerated sea water may be as low as 0.008 mm/yr at the same temperature (Figure 4.6) /14/. The corrosion allowance concept is based on the fact that the rate of transport of oxygen to waste canisters buried in marine sediments will be slow, and hence it is feasible to make allowance for corrosion losses by choosing an appropriate container wall thickness.

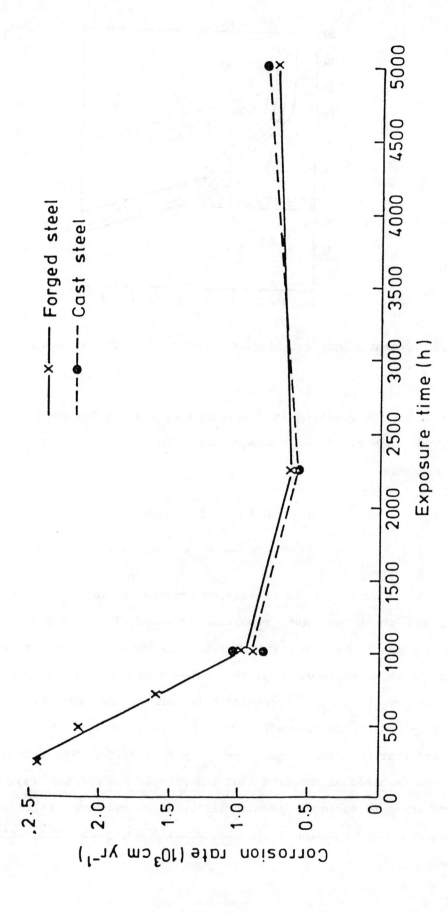

FIGURE 4.6. Corrosion rate in deaerated sea water.

From the above discussion it is clear that the effect of disposal temperature and pressure on the performance of carbon steel canisters must be considered in relation to their influence on the rates of the cathodic reactions (7)
and (8).

4.3.1 Oxygen Reduction

If oxygen transport is under diffusion control, the rate of the oxygen
reduction reaction at steady state will obey the expression:

$$i_{O_2} = \frac{F}{E} \; D \; \frac{C}{x} \qquad\qquad (4.9)$$

where i_0 is the reaction current density, E equivalent weight of O_2, F Fara-
days constant and D the diffusion coefficient of O_2 in the sediment. As an example, assuming disposal to a depth of 10 m at 25°C, and assuming the diffusion
coefficient for sediment is the same as for water (i.e. $D = 10^{-9} \; m^2 sec^{-1}$) and
the oxygen content of bottom sea water is 8 ppm, then i_0 will be
1.2×10^{-6} amps.m^{-2}. This is equivalent to a steel corrosion rate (i.e. as
$Fe(OH)_2$) of $\sim$ 0.001 μm/yr.

The diffusion coefficient of oxygen increases with temperature with an
activation energy of about 5.0 Kcals/mole, which means that the diffusion coefficient increases by 2% for every degree rise in temperature /15/. However,
this tendency for enhanced oxygen transport with increasing temperature will be
somewhat counter-attacked by the increase in oxygen activity which also occurs
with increasing temperature. This will reduce the activity gradient which supports oxygen diffusion, because the activity of oxygen will increase as it dif-
fuses up the temperature gradient towards the canister. The relative magnitudes
of these opposing effects needs to be determined before the influence of temperature can be quantified. A theoretical assessment is being made as part of

the UK programme on containment materials for marine disposal. Current results indicate that if oxygen transport occurs by diffusion alone, the rate of dissolution will quickly fall to a level which is only slightly higher than that observed in deaerated water (e.g. 0.008 mm/yr at 90°C).

An additional source of oxidizing species may be produced from the radiolytic decomposition of sea water. The significance of this source is difficult to assess because it will depend on the complex radiation chemistry of the sediment/sea water environment as well as on the radiation dose rate itself, which, in turn, will depend on the age and concentration of the waste, the separation of the canisters and the thickness of their walls. Tests have shown that a gamma-radiation dose rate of 1.5×10^5 Rads/h, which is the rate anticipated from 10 year old unprotected stored waste, will increase the steady state corrosion rate in deaerated sea water at 90°C from 0.008 to 0.044 mm/yr /14/. However, it is difficult to relate this result to the true situation because the tests were conducted in the absence of sediments, and the gas purging would facilitate the escape of the more mobile H_2 radiolysis products which may otherwise have accumulated and suppressed the radiolytic generation of oxidizing species. Furthermore, the result will be pessimistic because, in practice, the radiation dose rate will decay with time, and the thick walls of the canisters will have a significant attenuating effect. The effect of pressure and temperatures on the radiolysis of sediment/sea water environments has not been studied. Whilst it is unlikely that pressure "per se" should exert a significant influence, temperature could well change the comparative reaction rates of the various radiolysis products and, therefore, requires detailed investigation.

4.3.2 Water Reduction

Although the rate of supply of oxygen is usually the main factor in controlling the sea water corrosion of carbon steel, the preceding discussion has

shown that the sediment barrier may reduce this to a low level. In this circum-
stance, corrosion due to the water reduction cathodic reaction (7), although
low, could become a significant component over the lifetime of the canister
and, therefore, needs to be assessed.

Eq. (7) shows that the electrode potential of the water reduction reaction
is dependent on the partial pressure of hydrogen. If this increased from one
bar to 600 bars (i.e. the hydrostatic pressure at a depth of 7000 m), the electrode potential would be displaced negatively by $\sim$80 mV at 25°C. This analysis
gives a maximum estimate because it assumes that hydrogen generated by reaction
(7) will accumulate at the metal surface whereas, in practice, it will migrate
into the sediment. Nonetheless, even with this maximum estimate, Figure 15
shows that this is too small to alter the thermodynamic feasibility of the
oxidation of iron by deaerated water.

Turning to consider the rate of the water reduction reaction, unlike oxygen reduction, this will not be transport-limited, but will be under activation
control and can, therefore, be described by Tafel kinetics, i.e.:

$$i_{H_2O} = i_o \exp\left(\frac{-\beta F \eta}{RT}\right)$$ (4.10)

where i_{H_2O} is the reaction current density, i_o is a proportionality constant
which varies with temperature, β is the charge transfer coefficient and η the
electrode potential. Recent experimental studies in 3% NaCl solution have determined the water reduction reaction kinetics at 25 and 90°C which were /16/:

$$i_{H_2O}(25°C) = 6.5 \times 10^{-13} \exp\left[-0.43 \frac{\eta F}{RT}\right] \quad (\text{amps cm}^{-2})$$ (4.11)

$$i_{H_2O}(90°C) = 6.31 \times 10^{-11} \exp\left[-0.45 \frac{\eta F}{RT}\right] \quad (\text{amps cm}^{-2})$$ (4.12)

Using these data it has been estimated that the corrosion rate due to the water reduction cathodic reaction will be about 0.005 and 0.006 mm/yr for 25°C and 90°C, respectively /16/. This implies that the water reduction corrosion rate has a thermal activation energy of the order of 8 Kcals/mole. The estimated corrosion rate for 90°C is appreciably higher than that measured experimentally in deaerated sea water (i.e. 0.008 mm/yr), and it is believed that the discrepancy arises because, in practice, the steel surface becomes partially screened by corrosion product and carbonaceous deposits. The effect of pressure on the kinetics of the water reduction are uncertain. Some limited work at a hydrostatic pressure of 600 bar /17/ has only detected a margin effect, but these tests were conducted in a system in which hydrogen could easily escape into the bulk solution.

Despite the discrepancy referred to above, Eqs. (11) and (12) do indicate that the reduction of water occurs much more sluggishly on steel surfaces than it does on other metals such as platinum or nickel. However, certain compounds are known to increase the reaction rate and thereby could accelerate corrosion. The example most relevant to the present case is FeS, which is thought to act by absorbing H_2. Some FeS could be produced on the container surfaces if sulphides are present in the marine sediment, however, the supply is likely to be limited by diffusion. A more appreciable source of sulphide would be the presence of sulphate reducing bacteria on the container surface, however, there is no information on the microbial activity in deep ocean sediments if indeed there is any al all. Nor is there any information on the availability of suitable nutrients in the sediments should bacteria be introduced during the emplacement of the containers. Some information is available which suggests that sulphate-reducing bacteria sould not survive at temperatures exceeding 50°C and at pressures exceeding 500 bar /18/, but it is possible that these data are specified to the particular organisms tested.

Another factor which influences the rate of the water or hydrogen ion reduction reactions is pH. In particular the reaction rate increases significantly at pH values below 5. Under ambient conditions the pH of sea water is about 8.1, but at higher temperatures some of the dissolved salts hydrolyse causing the pH to fall. Table 4.2 /17/ shows the variation of the sea water pH with temperature, and clearly beyond 150°C quite significant acidity can be produced. If this effect also occurs in the pore water of marine sediments, the corrosion of carbon steel canisters should increase appreciably at disposal temperatures exceeding 150°C.

TABLE 4.2.   EFFECT OF TEMPERATURE ON THE pH OF SEA WATER /17/.

Temperature (°C)	pH[(*)]	Temperature (°C)	pH[(*)]
25	8.1	200	5.5
100	8.6	250	3.9
150	5.9	270	3.3

(*) pH measured after cool down.

It will be recalled that a general corrosion rate of 0.008/yr was measured in deaerated sea water at 90°C (Figure 4.5). In addition to thermally induced acidification, recent studies have shown that irradiation may also cause a reduction in the pH of sea water /16/. This second process is important because it occurs at lower temperatures (i.e. 90°C), and is currently the subject of further research.

To conclude, it would appear that mechanisms exist which could cause the acidification of sea water, but it is not clear whether the sediment will have sufficient pH buffering capacity to overcome these processes.

4.3.3 Influence of the Sea Sediments

At AERE Harwell /19/ a mechanistically based mathematical model was developed to predict the rate of general attack as a function of time and as a function of environmental parameters such as sediment depth, radiation dose rate and temperature. The model was based on the simplifying but conservative assumption that the kinetics of the principal electrochemical corrosion reactions (i.e. the dissolution of Fe and reduction of H_2O) were under activation control and were unimpeded by the sediment or the build up of corrosion product films on the metal surface.

The model required input data on the bare surface kinetics of the corrosion reactions and on the production of oxidising radiolysis products and these were determined experimentally. Overall reaction coefficients and exchange current densities for the anodic and cathodic reactions were determined at three temperatures and the results are given in Table 4.3. Additional studies were carried out to investigate the effect on the kinetics of pressure and of the presence of sulphide, but in both cases any effects were found to be negligible.

The model was first used to investigate the effect of sediment thickness on corrosion rate. The results obtained for the mean electrochemical kinetic data at 90°C, but disregarding irradiation effects, are shown in Figure 17. This indicates that the corrosion rate is not affected by sediment depths exceeding 100 mm, because steady state oxygen transport from the sediment surface ceases to be significant below this depth. The model has also been used to predict the steady corrosion rates, with a sediment cover of 500 mm, at constant temperatures of 20, 50 and 90°C. The results are given in Table 4.4. They have been evaluated using mean value electrochemical kinetic data and also a combination of anodic positive standard deviation and cathodic negative standard deviation data. This latter combination was used because preliminary calculations showed it to give the highest corrosion rates. Results including the effects of irradiation are also given. These are based on an initial dose rate of 10^5 Rad/h with an effective half life of 30 years, and are averaged over 1000

TABLE 4.3.   SUMMARY OF ELECTROCHEMICAL KINETIC DATA USED BY THE MATHEMATICAL MODEL.

Temp. (°C)	Data	Anodic reaction coefficient $(n\beta')$	Anodic exchange current density (Amps m^{-2})	Cathodic reaction coefficient $(n\ 1-\beta'')$	Cathodic exchange current density (Amps m^{-2})
25	M	1.08	3.17×10^{12}	0.43	9.75×10^{-9}
	M+ σ	1.32	5.67×10^{15}	0.49	6.72×10^{-10}
	M− σ	0.84	1.78×10^{9}	0.37	1.41×10^{-7}
50	M	1.24	2.46×10^{14}	0.49	2.17×10^{-8}
	M+ σ	1.64	1.16×10^{19}	0.55	2.51×10^{-9}
	M− σ	0.84	5.22×10^{9}	0.42	1.87×10^{-7}
90	M	1.55	1.14×10^{16}	0.53	1.14×10^{-7}
	M+ σ	1.80	2.67×10^{19}	0.63	3.93×10^{-9}
	M− σ	1.29	3.57×10^{12}	0.42	3.29×10^{-6}

M   = mean
σ   = standard deviation
β' = anodic charge transfer coefficient
β" = cathodic charge transfer coefficient
(*) = defined arbitrarily as the current at 0 mV (SCE).

TABLE 4.4. COMPARISON OF GENERAL CORROSION RATES PREDICTED BY THE MATHEMATICAL MODEL AND THOSE MEASURED EXPERIMENTALLY.

Temp. (°C)	Mathematical model predictions				Experiment results	
	Electrochemical kinetic data used	Condition	Steady rest potential (mV vs SCE)	Steady corrosion rate ($\mu m\ yr^{-1}$)	Steady rest potential (mV vs SCE)	Steady corrosion rate ($\mu m\ yr^{-1}$)
20	$M_a : M_c$	Inactive	-801	7.8	-800	2.1-2.2
20	$M_a + \sigma : M_c - \sigma$	Inactive	-790	13.4		
20	$M_a : M_c$	Radiation	-776	14.8		
20	$M_a + \sigma : M_c - \sigma$	Radiation	-776	20.4		
50	$M_a : M_c$	Inactive	-814	42.2	-790 (rising)	5.3-8.2
50	$M_a + \sigma : M_c - \sigma$	Inactive	-831	69.3		
50	$M_a : M_c$	Radiation	-808	49.2		
50	$M_a + \sigma : M_c - \sigma$	Radiation	-825	76.3		
90	$M_a : M_c$	Inactive	-793	89.9	-775 (rising)	16.8-21.6
90	$M_a + \sigma : M_c - \sigma$	Inactive	-803	208		
90	$M_a : M_c$	Radiation	-790	96.9		
90	$M_a + \sigma : M_c - \sigma$	Radiation	-801	215.9		

M_a = mean anodic data
M_c = mean cathodic data
σ = standard deviation.

TABLE 4.5. SUMMARY OF AVERAGE CORROSION RATES OBTAINED FROM LONG TERM SIMULA-
TION EXPERIMENTS.

Test period (days)	Material	Condition	Temperature (°C)	Average corrosion rate (μm yr^{-1})
878	Forged	Plain	20	2.2 $\pm$ 0.4
878	Forged	Weld	20	2.1 $\pm$ 0.4
879	Cast	Plain	20	2.2 $\pm$ 0.6
879	Cast	Weld	20	2.5 $\pm$ 0.4
885	Low carbon	Plain	20	3.1 $\pm$ 0.3
885	Low carbon	Weld	20	3.1 $\pm$ 0.5
1117	Forged	Plain	50	8.2 $\pm$ 0.9
1117	Forged	Weld	50	5.3 $\pm$ 0.3
1087	Cast	Plain	50	11.3 $\pm$ 2.3
1087	Cast	Weld	50	14.6 $\pm$ 2.7
960	Low carbon	Plain	50	12.0 $\pm$ 1.7
960	Low carbon	Weld	50	12.0 $\pm$ 1.1
948	Forged	Plain	90	16.8 $\pm$ 0.8
948	Forged	Weld	90	21.6 $\pm$ 3.1
941	Cast	Plain	90	10.6 $\pm$ 1.8
941	Cast	Weld	90	10.6 $\pm$ 1.6
908	Low carbon	Plain	90	11.0 $\pm$ 0.7
908	Low carbon	Weld	90	13.1 $\pm$ 2.9

$\pm$ indicates standard deviation of results from 10 specimens.

years. These results show that radiation increases the rate of corrosion only marginally. The effect of advective transport through the sediments was also investigated using the model, but the results indicated that the slow convection currents that may be induced by the decay heat from the waste should have no significant effect on corrosion rates.

Long term tests simulating the burial of carbon steel in marine sediment have been carried out for periods of up to 3.5 years to provide data to test the validity of the model's predictions. The tests were run at ambient temperature and at 50 and 90°C, and average corrosion rates determined from weight loss measurements are given in Table 4.5. These data indicate a significant increase in corrosion rate between about 20°C and 50°C, but only a small increase between 50 and 90°C. There is little difference between the dissolution rates of the three types of steel considered. Inspection of the specimens showed that some enhanced dissolution had occurred on the edges of the forged steel tested at 50 and 90°C. This form of corrosion was not apparent on either of the other two steels and is thought to be associated with metallurgical inhomogeneities. In addition, some pitting corrosion was found on the broad faces of some specimens from all three steels which had been tested at 50 and 90°C. This attack was most severe at locations where additions of distilled water, to make up evaporation losses, had eroded the sediment reducing the coverage over some specimens, and is thought to be due to increased transport of oxygen to the specimen surface.

The results of the tests are compared with the model predictions in Table 4.4. This shows that, in line with the conservative assumptions on which it is based, the model generally over-estimates the rate of attack at all three temperatures. It can therefore be used to make a conservative estimate of the allowance required to prevent waste containers being breached by general attack for a given period of time. From calculations of the temperature at the interface between waste containers and surrounding sediments as a function of time, it has been estimated that the interface temperature may be assumed to be 90°C for the first 50 years, 50°C for the next 50 years and about 20°C for the remainder of the container life. Using the highest of the corrosion rates predicted by the model and listed in Table 4.4. gives a corrosion allowance for a 1000 year container life of 33 mm. This should be a sufficiently conservative estimate to allow for any enhanced corrosion due to metallurgical differences, as observed on the edge faces of some specimens in the long term tests.

At JRC Ispra tests have been conducted putting in contact mild steel samples with two types of sea sediments /20/. The corrosion tests were performed in a closed system in which a column of sea sediments, wetted by its own interstitial water, was pressed against the mild steel sample.

The sea sediments used were of two different origins. The first one was obtained from the site Capoverde 2 (CV2). It is a sediment rich in carbonates, around 50%. The second one is a Pacific sea sediment (PC), rich in clay with a typical carbonate content of 0.3%. They have been stored in air at low temperature, around 4°C, for more than one year, so that it can be assumed that they are saturated with oxygen. Using CV2 sediments, tests have been conducted at 30, 50 and 90°C up to a maximum time of 200 days. The specific weight losses are exposed in Figures 4.8 and 4.9.

Assuming that the reaction corresponding to the depolarization by the small amount of oxygen dissolved in the interstitial sea water is instantaneous and that the anoxic corrosion proceeds linearly with time, the experimental data have been analysed, by the use of a least square best fitting routine, following the equation:

$$\Delta W = a + bt \tag{4.13}$$

Table 4.6 gives the values of the parameters obtained.

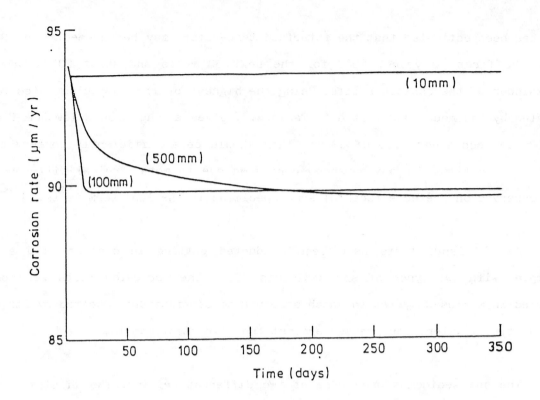

FIGURE 4.7. Mathematical model predictions of the effect of sediment coverage on the general corrosion of carbon steel at 90°C.

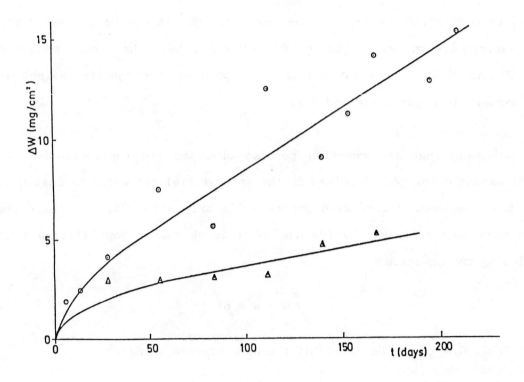

FIGURE 4.8. Corrosion weight losses of mild steel samples in contact with CV2 sediments; Δ 30°C, ⊙ 50°C.

TABLE 4.6.   CORROSION IN SEA SEDIMENTS.

Temperature (°C)	$a(gr/cm^2)$	$b(gr/cm^2)$	$a'(\mu m)$	$b'(\mu m/y)$
30 (CV2)	$2 \cdot 10^{-3}$	$1.6 \cdot 10^{-5}$	2.6	7.8
50 (CV2)	$2.3 \cdot 10^{-3}$	$6.2 \cdot 10^{-5}$	3.0	29.4
90 (CV2)	$7.8 \cdot 10^{-3}$	$2.0 \cdot 10^{-4}$	10	95.4
90 (PC)	$3.3 \cdot 10^{-2}$	$5.7 \cdot 10^{-5}$	42.3	27.2

Comparison tests have been conducted using the red clay sea sediments only at 90°C up to the same maximum exposure time. In order to verify if some oxygen diffusion was arising through the seals of the apparatus, some tests in red clay sediments were performed introducing the apparatus in a thermostat filled with nitrogen. The results are exposed in Figure 4.9. It can be seen that the values of the corrosion for the samples which were kept in a thermostat filled with nitrogen are in excellent agreement with those obtained with the samples kept in air thermostat. We can conclude that the system used is tight and that the corrosion is not influenced by the external atmosphere.

Comparing the results obtained using the two different sediments (Table 4.6), it can be seen that in the first period the weight losses can be considered comparable while in the second period the corrosion rate in the PC sediments decreases sharply.

It is interesting to compare the results obtained using the Harwell mathematical model with those obtained in this experimental work. It can be noted that the values obtained with the carbonaceous sediments are very near to those indicated in Table 4.4 as predicted by the mathematical model. On the contrary they are higher than those obtained in the simulation experiments. The results obtained with the clay sediments are on the contrary of the same order of magnitude of the Harwell experimental data.

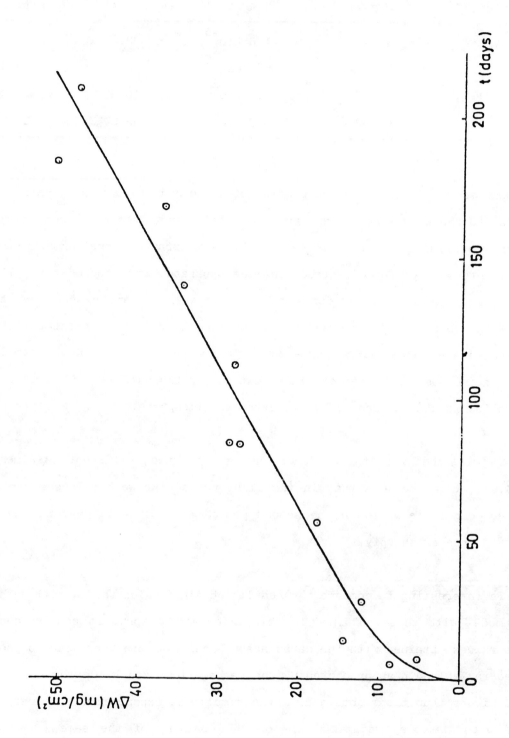

FIGURE 4.9. Corrosion weight losses of mild steel samples in contact with CV2 sediments; 90°C.

An evaluation of the dependence of the reaction from temperature has been performed (Figure 4.11) assuming that the linear corrosion rate, as expressed by the "b" coefficient, depends on temperature following an Arrhenius law. It can be seen that the curves corresponding to the corrosion in clay and in sea sediments have different slopes. A calculation of the corresponding activation energies gives for the clay a value of 3300 cal/mole and for the CV2 sediments 9100 cal/mole. Such a large difference induces to take into consideration that two different corrosion mechanisms are present.

A best fitting analysis of the linear coefficients obtained in the tests using CV2 sediments has given the following result:

$$b = 76.5 \exp (9080/RT) \ (gr/cm^2 d) \tag{4.14}$$

It is possible that such a high corrosion rate is transitory and that in the long term lower values, as found in other systems, are obtained. Tests of longer duration are needed to clarify this point.

During the first period of the permanence of the waste package in the sea sediments around the canister or the overcoating, a thermal gradient will be present. It seemed interesting to verify if such a condition has an influence on the homogeneous corrosion rate. In fact, the corrosion of the mild steel is strongly influenced by the diffusion of oxygen present in the sediment interstitial sea water and also by the diffusion of hydrogen generated in the anoxic corrosion. It is then possible that the diffusion will be altered by the thermal gradient (Soret effect).

Some tests have been conducted in the Ispra laboratories in an apparatus which imposes on the sediments a thermal gradient of 1°C/cm. Preliminary results seem to indicate that in such a condition the corrosion rate is lower than that encountered in isothermal conditions. In particular on the surface a precipitation of calcium carbonate is observed which could protect mechanically

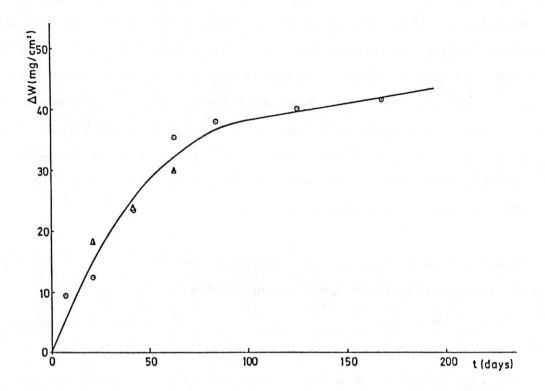

FIGURE 4.10. Corrosion weight losses of mild steel samples in contact with Pacific clay sediments; 90°C - ▲ test performed in a nitrogen filled thermostat.

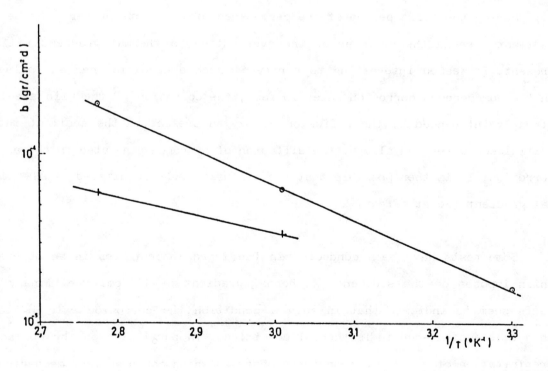

FIGURE 4.11. Variation with temperature of the b coefficient; + tests in Boom clay, ⊙ tests in CV2 sediments.

the surface. Longer tests are needed to verify the importance of such an effect.

CV2 sediment columns corresponding to corrosion experiments of 84 and 210 day duration at 50 and 90°C have been analysed for the iron content. Assuming that the flow of corrosion product is constant and that the column is infinite, the distribution of iron concentration, C, can be expressed by the following equation /21/:

$$C = 2 \, F_g/D \, \text{ierfc}(x/2\sqrt{Dt}) \qquad (4.15)$$

where D is the diffusion coefficient, F_g the constant flow at the interface, x is the distance from the interface. The corresponding diffusion coefficients D and mass flow F_g obtained using a best fitting routine at the interface are exposed in Table 4.7. It is interesting to note that the F_g values correspond rather well to the linear corrosion rate indicating that all the corrosion products corresponding to the anoxic condition are soluble and contribute to the concentration distribution.

TABLE 4.7.   DIFFUSION IN CV2 SEDIMENTS.

Temp. (°C)	b(gr/cm^{2}d)	84 days		210 days	
		F_g(gr/cm^{2}d)	D(cm^2/s)	F_g(gr/cm^{2}d)	D(cm^2/s)
50	$6.2 \cdot 10^{-5}$	$5.9 \cdot 10^{-5}$	$5 \cdot 10^{-8}$	$4.5 \cdot 10^{-5}$	$2.4 \cdot 10^{-8}$
90	$2.0 \cdot 10^{-4}$	$2.1 \cdot 10^{-4}$	$4.0 \cdot 10^{-8}$	$1.9 \cdot 10^{-4}$	$2.0 \cdot 10^{-8}$

An evaluation of the diffusion coefficient of Fe^{2+} in free sea water obtained from the data exposed in /22/ gives at 80°C a value of 2.5×10^{-5} cm^2/s. From our diffusion results, which give a mean value of 3×10^{-8} cm^2/s it is possible to calculate a mean retardation factor of about 800. It appears clearly that the iron species generated during the corrosion process are strongly absorbed.

4.3.4 Localized Corrosion

An stated previously, carbon steels do not develop a true passive oxide layer in sea water, and consequently they are less liable to film breakdown and localized corrosion than the titanium alloys discussed prevously. Nonetheless, pitting corrosion has been experienced with carbon steels in some sea water applications /10/. These examples, however, all involve aerated conditions and hence the potential for establishing local deaeration cells. Significantly experience with hot deaerated sea water in desalination plant, which is more relevant to the canister environment, suggests that pitting should not be a problem /10/.

Localized corrosion could possibly occur if the corrosion properties of the sealing welds were different to that of the canisters. This should not be a problem, however, if good standard welding procedures are adopted.

Another form of localized attack which needs to be considered is environmentally assisted cracking (i.e. hydrogen embrittlement or stress corrosion cracking). This only occurs in metal subject to tensile stressing, therefore the comments made in Section 4.2.3 on the possible beneficial effect of the high hydrostatic pressures involved in marine disposal apply equally here. Environmental cracking in sea water is usually restricted to high strength steels, therefore, if the waste canisters are fabricated from plain low-carbon steel they should be resistant to attack. High hardness welds also represent regions of potential susceptibility, particularly if the environment is contaminated by $S^=$ species which enhance absorption. This can be avoided by using a steel with a sufficiently low carbon equivalent, alternatively, the canisters could be given a post-weld heat treatment.

4.4 Conclusions

a) The titanium base alloys currently being considered for waste canisters should have a high resistance to general attack at temperatures up to 250°C, with average dissolution rates not exceeding 12.0 μm/yr. Bearing in mind that passive corrosion normally exhibits parabolic rather than linear kinetics, this rate – derived from short-term tests – should be pessimistic. However, the long-term stability of the TiO_2 surface film responsible for this corrosion resistance needs to be established.

b) Commercial purity titanium should also have a high resistance to general corrosion as long as the environment is not strongly reducing.

c) Both commercial purity titanium and the titanium base alloys are likely to be susceptible to crevice corrosion if the sea water temperature is sufficiently high. This could lead to rapid local dissolution. Tests with metal/metal crevices indicate that CP titanium and the Ti-0.2Pd alloy may be subject to attack at temperatures exceeding 130 and 170°C, respectively. However, these data should be pessimistic because the crevices produced at the interface between canisters and seabed sediments should be less severe.

d) Titanium and its alloys may be subject to hydrogen embrittlement. This is most likely to occur under reducing conditions, but could also occur under oxidizing conditions due to radiolytically generated hydrogen. Hydrogen pick-up will be accelerated by high disposal temperatures, but cracking is unlikely to occur until the canisters have cooled below 100°C.

e) The titanium alloys under consideration for waste canisters are generally resistant to stress corrosion cracking. However, no information is available on their long-term behaviour at high disposal temperatures.

f) At moderate temperatures (i.e. up to 100°C) the general corrosion of carbon steel is normally controlled by the rate of transport of oxygen and other oxidizing species. However, in the case of waste containers the rate of oxygen diffusion is so low that corrosion by direct reaction with water is dominant. Laboratory tests in deaerated sea water under inactive conditions have indicated a corrosion rate of the order of 0.008 mm/yr at 90°C.

g) A mechanistically based mathematical model was developed in order to evaluate a conservative estimation of the iron homogeneous corrosion. Using this value and taking into account the temperature evolution of the iron-sediments interface it appears that a thickness of 33 mm would give a corrosion allowance for 1000 years.

Tests performed in carbonaceous sea sediments have given values which are higher than those obtained for other porous media but very near to those obtained using the above mentioned mathematical model.

h) At disposal temperatures exceeding 150°C sea water becomes increasingly acidic, and this raises the possibility that the carbon steel corrosion rate could be appreciably higher than that anticipated at temperatures below 100°C. At present it is not known whether the marine sediments have sufficient pH "buffering" capacity to counteract this effect.

i) Carbon steel canisters are unlikely to be subject to significant pitting corrosion under the low oxygen conditions anticipated in marine sediments.

l) It is unlikely that the carbon steel canisters will be subject to stress corrosion cracking. One possible area of susceptibility is the hard metallurgical structures produced in sealing welds. These should be avoided by using steels with an appropriately low carbon equivalent or by heat treating the canisters after sealing.

References

/1/ Marsh, G.P. (1982). Materials for the containment of high level waste. Abl. 21, No. 4, 253-265.

/2/ Stein, M. and Wiesenberg, H. (1959). The influence of noble metal alloy additions on the electrochemical and corrosion behaviour of titanium. J. Electrochem. Soc., Vol. 106, p. 759.

/3/ Stranmanis, M.E., Shil, S.T. and Schleckten, A.W. (1955). Hydrogen over-voltage of titanium in acidic and basic solutions. J. Phys. Chem., 50, 317.

/4/ Naish, C.C. and Marsh, G.P. (1983). Corrosion resistant containment materials for high level nuclear waste. AERE-R10775, February 1983.

/5/ Ulanovskii, I.B. (1976). Corrosion of steel, titanium and copper at various depths in the Black Sea. Protection of Metals, 12 (4), pp. 394-395, July-August 1976.

/6/ Bomberger, H.B., Cambourelis, P.J. and Hutchinson, G.E. (1954). Corrosion properties of titanium in marine environments. J. Electrochem. Soc., 101 (9), pp. 442-447.

/7/ Reinhart, F.M. (1967). Technical Note N-921, US Naval Civil Eng. Lab., Port Hueneme, California.

/8/ Charlot, L.A. (1970). Investigation of galvanically induced hydriding of Ti in saline solutions. US Dept. of the Interior R&D Report No. 624, December 1970.

/9/ Braithwaite, J.W., Magnani, N.J. and Munford, J.W. (1980). Titanium alloy corrosion in nuclear waste environments. Paper 214, Corrosion 80, NACE, Chicago, USA.

/10/ Sea water Corrosion Handbook, Editor M. Schumacher, published by Noted Data Corporation, New Jersay, USA.

/11/ Blundy, R.F. and Shrier, L.L. (1969). Permeation of hydrogen through iron during cathodic polarisation under hydrostatic pressure. Phil. Mag., 20 (168), pp. 77-87.

/12/ Caskey, G.R. (1974). Diffusion of tritium in rutile (TiO_2). Materials Science and Engineering, Vol. 13 (2), pp. 109-115.

/13/ Jackson, J.D. and Boyd, W.K. (1968). Crevice corrosion of titanium. Edited by M. Lipitt, Int. Conf. on the Science, Technology and Applications of Titanium, pp. 267-281, London 1968.

/14/ Marsh, G.P., Bland, I.W., Desport, J.A., Naish, C.C., Westcott, C. and Taylor, K.J. (1983). Corrosion assessment of metal overpacks for radioactive waste disposal. Eur. Appl. Res. Reports, Vol. 4 (2), pp. 224-252.

/15/ Hitchman, M.L. (1978). Measurement of dissolved oxygen. Published by J.Wiley, New York, London 1978.

/16/ Taylor, K.J., Bland, I.D. and Marsh, G.P. (1984). Corrosion studies on HLW-canister materials for marine disposal. AERE-G2971, July 1984.

/17/ Molecke, M.A., Shaefer, D.W., Glass, R.S. and Rupper, J.A.. To be published in Advances in Science and Technology of the Management of High Level Nuclear Waste, Vol. 1.

/18/ Tiller, A.K. (1983). Is stainless steel susceptible to microbial corrosion?. In Proc. of Conf. on Microbial Corrosion, National Physical Laboratory, Teddington, March 1983.

/19/ Marsh, G.P., Harker, A.H. and Taylor, K.J. (1987). Corrosion of carbon steel nuclear waste containers in marine sediments. AERE R12510, Harwell.

/20/ Lanza, F. and Ronsecco, C. (1986). Corrosion of low carbon steel in clay and sea sediments. EUR 10522 EN, Ispra 1986.

/21/ Carslaw, H.S. and Jaeger, J.C.J. (1959). Conduction of heat in solids. p. 75, Clarendon Press.

/22/ Yuen-Hin Li and Gregory, S. (1974). Diffusion of ions in sea water and deep sea sediments. Geochim. and Cosmochim. Acta, 28, pp. 703-714.

CHAPTER 5: WASTE FORM LEACHING

5.1 Introduction

The disposal of a waste package into the sea sediments can be considered a relatively simple system. In fact, the system will be composed only of the glass, the canister material and the sediments. No structural material or back-filling are to be taken into consideration. Usually, two possibilities are investigated for the canister material. A material, such as for instance Ticode 12, having a high resistance to corrosion due to the formation of a very stable oxide. Alternatively, the use of a material, such as mild iron, is also fore-seen. In the first case we can assume that the stable oxide does not interfere with the glass or with the released elements. In this condition, the release and migration of the elements will depend only on the interaction between the glass and the sediments wetted by sea water. In the second case, a large amount of corrosion products will also be present. However, corrosion tests /1/ have shown that most of the corrosion products are in a soluble form and can diffuse into the sediment mass. As a consequence, in this case the glasses will be in contact with the sediments which have adsorbed the mild steel corrosion products.

As underlined in the general introduction we will consider that the container will last for the so-called thermal period, so that when the glass, after the dissolution or the disintegration of the container, will come in contact with the sea sediments, no thermal gradient will be present. Apart from this, the gamma activity will be reduced to a negligible level. The main activity present will be the soft beta due to the long life fission products and to the alpha emitted by the actinides. As a consequence, the leaching of the glass will arrive in isothermal conditions at a temperature probably slightly higher than that of the undisturbed condition ($\sim 2°C$). The most important radiation effect will be the damage to the glass due to alpha radiation and to the recoil of the alpha emitters which could decrease the resistance of the glass to the leaching.

Obviously, in the accidental case it is possible that a premature failure of the canister arrives so that the leaching arrives in the presence of a field and of a thermal gradient. Tests have been conducted only in isothermal conditions. For the other conditions, only general considerations will be presented.

5.2 Glass Matrix

All the countries with reprocessing plants giving rise to High Level Waste (HLW) seem to have decided on borosilicate glass as the first generation solidification medium.

The compositions of the glasses to be used by the various countries depend on several factors. The fission product spectra arising from the different reactors (PWR, BWR, Magnox, etc.) are sufficiently similar chemically that this is not a mojor factor in the choice of glass composition. Much more important are the "tramp elements" that are included in the waste. For example, calcined waste from reprocessing Magnox reactor fuel contains only 40% fission product oxides, together with 25 wt% MgO, 20 wt% Al_2O_3 and 11 wt% Fe_2O_3. Waste from LWR fuel reprocessing could or could not contain a large amount (ca. 30 wt%) of Gd_2O_3 which is added to the dissolver as a neutron poison. Another important factor is the operation temperature of the glass melting furnace that is used. For example, the Harvest system that was originally proposed for use in the UK restricted the glass formation temperature to about 950°C; this meant that the glass composition chosen was relatively low in silica. As a general rule, the higher the formation temperature of a glass, the better is its leach resistance.

The glass compositions, suggested for HLW solidification in general are fairly similar, containing about 50 wt% SiO_2 and about 10-20 wt% of non-volatile fission product oxides. Some years ago the tendency was to include as high a proportion of fission products as possible to reduce the total volume of vitrified waste. At present, lower loadings are suggested so that the heat flux does not result in high temperatures during production or storage of the glass or after disposal.

A review of the influence of glass composition on the resistance to corrosion and leaching, can be found in Ref. /2/.

During the programme it was decided to use for the vitrified waste the same specification as in the PAGIS programme of the Commission of the European Cummunity. Table 5.1 gives the general characteristic and Table 5.2 gives the detailed composition of the glass.

The gaseous fission products (Kr and Xe) and almost all the iodine escape from the dissolver and are not present in the borosilicate glasses. Studies have been conducted on specific matrix for conditioning these elements /3,4/. For the safety assessment it is assumed that the noble gases will be sent to a separate storage. As for iodine, 0.1% of the inventory will be considered to be conditioned in the glass while the remaining part is considered to be present in the repository in an easily soluble form.

5.3 Tests in Sea Sediments

Usually, in the examination of the corrosion and leaching of glasses, a distinction is made between static and dynamic conditions. In a static condition, the elements which are leached, stay in the leachate so that phenomena such as alteration of the pH or saturation effects and reprecipitation of new compounds, can arrive.

TABLE 5.1. GENERAL CHARACTERISTIC OF THE VITRIFIED MLW.

Glass	: SON 68 18 17 L1 C2 A2 Z1
Reactor type	: LWR
Nominal electric power per reactor	: 0.9 GW(e)
Average specific power	: 33 MW(th)/tHM
Fuel type	: UO_2
Initial average enrichment (assembly)	: 3.5% U-235
Irradiation time	: 1000 days
Burn-up	: 33 GW.d(th)/tHM or 90.4 MW/(th).a/tHM
Residence time in reactor	: 36 months
Delay before reprocessing	: 3 years
Delay before HLW vitrification	: 1 year
Volume of reprocessed solution	: 0.661 m^3/tHM
Volume of glass	: 0.108 m^3/tHM
Density of glass	: 2.750 kg/m^3
Arising of waste	: 38 kg/tHM
Residual heat of glass after vitrification:	
after 2 years	: 11.633 KW/m^3
after 30 years	: 4.333 KW/m^3
after 100 years	: 1.0 KW/m^3
Amount of electric energy produced:	
by 1 tHM	: 30 MW(e).a/tHM
by 1 m^3 of glass	: 278 MW(e).a/m^3 glass
Amount of waste to be disposed of	: 3000 GW(e).a (approximately 3.333 reactor-years)
Resulting volume of glass to be disposed of	: 11.000 m^3
Date of disposal	: 50 years after vitrification

TABLE 5.2a. COMPOSITION OF THE GLASS IN kg/m^3.

SiO_2	1.241.39	Fe_2O_3	79.44
Al_2O_3	133.97	NiO	11.32
B_2O_3	382.83	Cr_2O_3	13.77
Na_2O	269.05	P_2O_5	7.71
CaO	110.29	ZrO_2	27.30
FP oxides	307.12	Li_2O	54.10
Act. oxides	23.32	ZnO	68.30
		Metal	19.10

Total: 2.749 kg/m^3

In a dynamic condition, the continuous flow of the leachant could maintain a constant composition of the aqueous solution and even, for higher flow rate, have a mechanical effect on the surface layer, giving rise to colloid formation. However, when the glass is immersed in a porous medium such as sea sediments, we are in a condition which is intermediate between the two. On the one hand, convection flow is strongly limited or even absent; on the other hand, the elements which come out of the glass can migrate by diffusion. As a consequence, the possible saturation effect and reprecipitation will depend mainly on the diffusion of the various elements in the porous medium.

In order to perform the tests, an apparatus has been set up which allows to keep a column of sediments in contact with a glass sample (Figure 5.1). In order to ensure that a good contact exists, the sediment column is pressed at a maximum pressure of 2.5 MPa by means of a hydraulic piston. The system is kept very tight so that no losses of the interstitial sea water can occur. A detailed description of the apparatus can be found in Ref. /5/.

The sediments are originated by the site Capo Verde 2 /6/, and are rich in carbonates, around 45%, but relatively poor in clay.

TABLE 5.2b.   COMPOSITION OF THE FISSION PRODUCTS PRESENT IN THE GLASS.

Element	Metal kg/m^3	Oxide kg/m^3	Element	Metal kg/m^3	Oxide kg/m^3
Se as SeO_2	0.506	0.713	In as In_2O_3	0.014	0.019
Rb as Rb_2O_3	3.259	3.565	Sn as SnO_2	0.396	0.500
Sr as SrO	7.696	9.102	Sn* as metal	0.061	–
Y as Y_2O_3	4.276	5.426	Sb as Sb_2O_3	0.079	0.093
Zr as $ZrOb_2$	33.315	45.009	Te as TeO_2	4.376	5.472
Nb as Nb_2O_3	0	0	Cs as CsO_2	33.231	35.231
Mo as MoO_3	21.263	31.926	Ba as BaO	14.824	16.556
Mo* as MoO_3	9.609	14.444	La as La_2O_3	11.157	13.083
Tc as TcO_2	5.222	6.907	Ce as Ce_2O_3	21.648	25.352
Tc* as metal	2.326	–	Pr as Pr_2O_3	10.269	12.019
Ru as RuO_2	9.694	12.833	Nd as Nd_2O_3	37.167	43.370
Ru* as metal	10.282	–	Pm as Pm_2O_3	0.611	0.713
Rh as Rh_2O_3	2.683	3.306	Sm as Sm_2O_3	7.380	8.556
Rh* as metal	1.836	–	Eu as Eu_2O_3	1.205	1.398
Pd as PdO	7.896	9.102	Cd as Cd_2O_3	0.711	0.824
Pd* as metal	3.672	–	Tb as Tb_2O_3	0.017	0.019
Ag as Ag_2O	0.709	0.759	Dy as Dy_2O_3	0.008	0.009
Cd as CdO	0.718	0.824			

Total oxides = 307.130 kg/m^3 Total FP metals = 18.177 kg/m^3

* From dissolution residues.

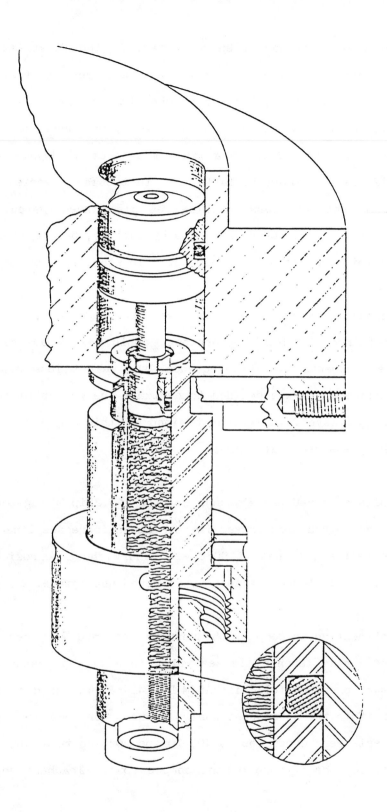

FIGURE 5.1.   Scheme of the apparatus for leaching tests of glass in
              contact with the sea sediments.

Two series of tests have been conducted. In the first one, borosilicate glass I117 was used; the leaching tests have been performed at 50°C up to a maximum time of 220 days. In the second one, borosilicate glass SON 68j, containing simulated fission products and actinides, was used; the leaching tests have been performed at 75°C up to a maximum time of 80 days. The compositions of the two glasses are given in Table 5.3. In the first series, the influence of corrosion products on glass leaching was also investigated. The sediments were charged with iron corrosion products by putting, before leaching, the sediment columns into contact with samples of mild steel for 165 days at 80°C.

When the glass was put into contact with the sediments, the surface layer, which resulted from the leaching process, could easily absorb products contained in the sediments. As a consequence, the weight loss measurements were not very significant. It was decided to evaluate the weight losses after having taken out the gel layer. The value obtained in this way can be considered a measure of the glass degradation rate.

The results obtained are exposed in Figure 5.2 in a log-log plot. It can be seen that the degradation losses in both cases increases linearly with time. Comparing the values obtained at 50°C with and without corrosion products, it appears that their influence is to be considered negligible.

It is interesting to compare the results obtained with sea sediments with those obtained during leaching in sea water in a closed system /5/. Synthetic sea water (ssw), prepared following ASTM DI 141-52, was used as a leachant. In order to facilitate the subsequent analysis, no boron compounds were introduced in the ssw. Tests were conducted at 40, 70 and 90°C up to a maximum time of 120 days. The ratio of the surface of the sample to the leachant volume ratio was 0.5 cm^{-1}.

It is particularly interesting to examine the equivalent weight losses of boron obtained through the analysis of boron in the leachate. It has been

TABLE 5.3. COMPOSITION OF SIMULATED GLASSES.

Oxyde	I117	SON 68s	Oxyde	I117	SON 68s
SiO_2	48.00	45.48	MoO_3	0.16	1.70
Al_2O_3	5.00	4.91	MnO_2	1.35	0.72
B_2O_3	15.00	14.02	CoO	1.63	0.12
Na_2O	15.9	9.86	Ag_2O		0.03
CaO		4.04	CdO		0.03
K_2O	1.38	0.85	SnO	0.03	0.02
Fe_2O_3	1.62	2.91	TeO_2		0.23
NiO	0.32	0.74	Cs_2O	3.53	1.29
Cr_2O_3		0.51	BaO	0.33	0.61
P_2O_5		0.28	La_2O_3	0.68	0.90
Li_2O		1.98	Pr_2O_3	0.31	0.44
ZnO	0.03	2.5	Nd_2O_3	0.69	1.29
Rb_2O		0.13	CeO_2	0.76	0.93
SrO	0.22	0.33	Sm_2O_3	1.12	
Y_2O_3	1.28	0.20	Eu_2O_3	0.3	0.3
ZrO_2	1.06	2.65	U_3O_8	1.38	1.8

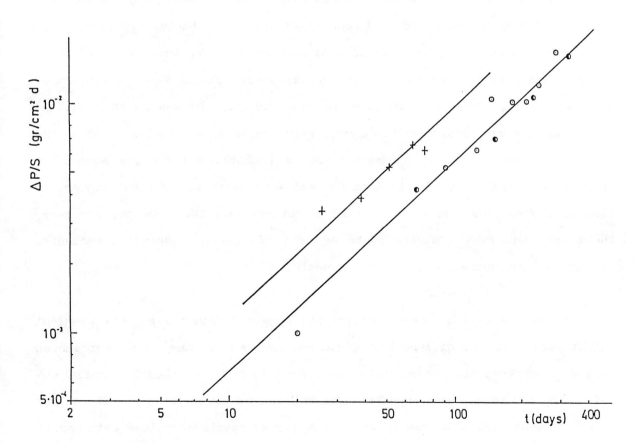

FIGURE 5.2. Degradation weight losses as a function of time; + glass SON 68s; ⊙ glass I117; ◑ glass I117
tested in a thermostat filled with argon.

pointed out /7/ that boron is the best indicator for the glass degradation. As a matter of fact, boron compounds are quite soluble so that, as soon as they are freed by the degradation of the glass silica matrix, they pass readily in solution. The results are exposed in Figure 5.3 for the I117 glass and in Figure 5.4 for the SON 68s glass. In both cases the plot of boron equivalent weight losses can be divided into two parts. At the beginning, at all temperatures, the attack is quite rapid and proceeds linearly with time. Successively, at 70 and 90°C, the weight loss rate decreases progressively.

An analysis of this part of the curve following a time power law shows an exponential of the order of 0.3, indicating that, in this phase, the leaching is governed by the reprecipitation of some compounds. The analysis of the surface layer by XPS indicates an enrichment of aluminium and magnesium.

It appears then reasonable to assume that the long-term degradation rate is controlled by the formation and reprecipitation of a complex magnesium silicate. J.H. Thomassin /8/ in his study of the surface degradation of basaltic glasses, was able to identify in the surface layer complex Mg-Al silicates as serpentines. Unfortunately, the layer obtained in our test was so thin that no X-ray analysis was possible. This phase, when leaching is arriving in the presence of sediments, is not present. This is probably due to the absorptive properties of the sediments which do not allow to reach a sufficient concentration of the various elements to obtain a saturation effect. On the contrary, the linear part of the static tests seems to follow a dissolution mechanism similar to that encountered in the sediments.

An analysis of the linear coefficients obtained from the boron equivalent weight losses at the different temperatures shows that they can be arranged following an Arrhenius relationship (Figure 5.5). The degradation rates obtained for the two glasses when leaching is conducted with the glass in contact with the sediments, fits rather well with the extrapolated values obtained by

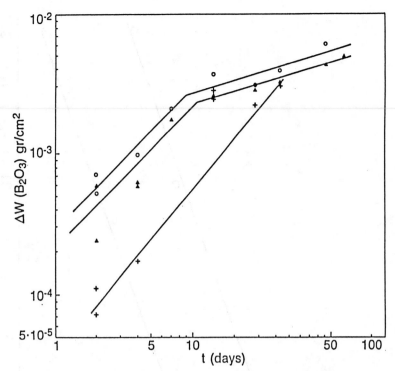

FIGURE 5.3.   Boron oxide equivalent weight losses of the glass I117 as a
function of time; + T = 40°C;   ▲T = 70°C; ΘT = 90°C.

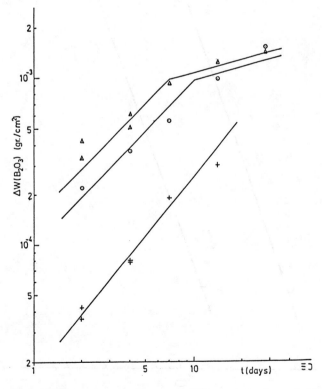

FIGURE 5.4.   Boron oxide equivalent weight losses of the glass SON 68s as
a function of time; + T = 40°C; ΘT = 70°C;   ΔT = 90°C.

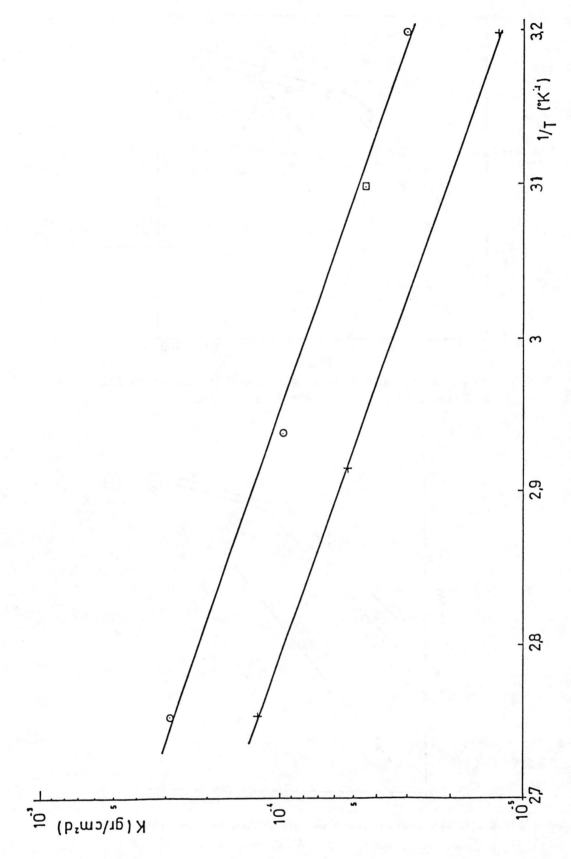

FIGURE 5.5. Dependence of the boron oxide equivalent weight loss rate and of the glass degradation rate on temperature; ⊙ glass I117; + glass SON 68s.

the Arrhenius plots. The assumption that the specific action of the sediments is to avoid saturation effects is then verified.

A best fitting of the experimental points gives for the two glasses the following relationships:

$$I117 \quad K = 238 \exp(-9900/RT) \qquad (gr/cm^2 d) \qquad (5.1)$$

$$SON\ 68s \quad K = 37 \exp(-8900/RT) \qquad (gr/cm^2 d) \qquad (5.2)$$

The activation energies are rather similar. The glass SON 68s represents a better resistance to leaching.

5.4 Release of Different Elements in the Sediments

On the tests performed with the I117 glass at 50°C, an analysis of the distribution of the different elements in the sediment column has been performed /5/. The column was cut successively, starting from the glass-sediments interface and the various slices were analysed by the neutron activation technique. The concentration distribution of various elements was studied in order to define the release mechanism and the diffusion coefficients in the sediments.

It can be assumed that all elements comprised in the glass are put in a condition of mobility by the degradation of the glass. In order to be able to evaluate the release of the different elements, it is worth classifying them following their solubility limit. Two classes can be defined:

- Elements forming compounds of elevated solubility which, once freed from the glass matrix, enter in the solution. Their release rate will be proportional to the degradation rate of the glass. Due to the small influence of diffusion into the glass /9/, also alkali belong to this class;

- Elements whose concentration in the solution is defined by the solubility product of the more stable phase. Their release does not depend on the degradation rate. The excess of the element freed from the glass stays on the surface either adsorbed on the gel layer or in a reprecipitated form.

In the first case, assuming that the diffusion coefficients of the various elements are independent from concentration, the Fick's second law of diffusion can be integrated having as a boundary condition:

$$-D_i \frac{\partial c_i}{\partial x}\bigg|_{x=0} = \phi_i \tag{5.3}$$

where ϕ_i in the flux of the element i at the interface between the glass and the sediments, and c_i its concentration at the distance x from the glass-sediments interface. For an infinite column, the distribution of the concentration is expressed /10/ by the following equation:

$$c_i = 2\phi_i \sqrt{t/D_i} \ \text{ierfc} \ (x/2\sqrt{D_i \cdot t}) \tag{5.4}$$

It has to be noted that the flux ϕ_i is related to the degradation rate of the glass k by the following relationship:

$$\phi_i = K \cdot \chi_i \tag{5.5}$$

where χ_i is the weight fraction of the i element present in the glass.

A typical element which is released following a constant flow boundary condition is cesium. The experimental value has been analysed using a best fitting routine which allows to calculate, following Eq. (5.5), the most probable data of k and D.

The k value obtained for cesium is 6.4×10^{-5} $gr/cm^2 d$ which compares favourably with the value (4.5×10^{-5}) obtained previously by the analysis of the weight losses of the glass sample. The assumption that the soluble elements are released as soon as the glass is degraded is then confirmed.

In order to avoid the scattering due to the variation in the degradation rate of the different samples, the concentrations of the various tests have been normalized to the mean k value. In Figure 5.6 are reported the normalized data obtained after 21, 49, 70 and 81 days, together with the theoretical curves as obtained by the best fitting of Eq. (5.5). It can be seen that the agreement is quite good.

For the elements whose concentration in the solution is determined by the solubility limit of a compound, it can be assumed as a boundary condition of the Fick's second law that at the interface between the glass and the sediments, the concentration of the element C_o is constant. Assuming that the diffusion coefficient does not depend on concentration and that the column can be considered infinite, we obtain a distribution of the concentrations of the type /11/:

$$C = C_o \ \text{erfc} \ (x/2\sqrt{Dt}) \qquad\qquad (5.6)$$

It has to be noted that in this case, even if the degradation of the glass increases linearly, the amount of released elements Q increases with the square root of time

$$Q = 2C_o \sqrt{Dt}/\pi \qquad\qquad (5.7)$$

As a consequence, the release rate will decrease progressively in time.

An example of an element which is released following a boundary condition of a maximum concentration is uranium. In Figure 5.7 are reported the experimental data and the theoretical curve obtained using the best fitting routine.

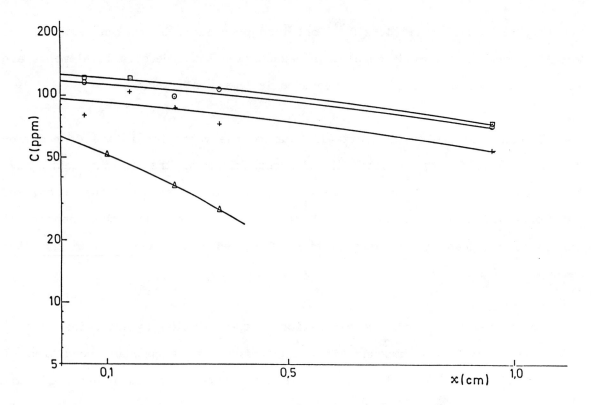

FIGURE 5.6. Distribution of cesium in the sediments for different exposure times; Δt = 21; + t = 49; Θt = 70; Ɵt = 81 days.

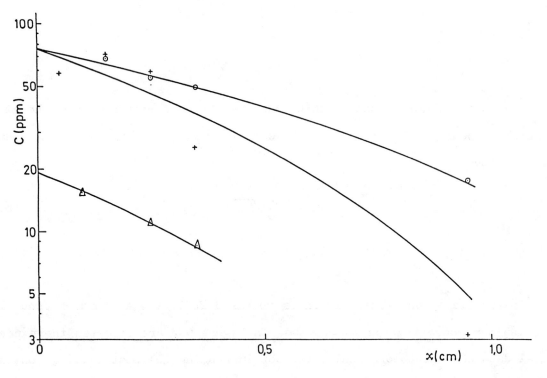

FIGURE 5.7. Distribution of uranium in the sediments for different exposure times; Δt = 21; + t = 49; Θt = 70 days.

The mean value of the maximum concentration is 78 ppm which corresponds to a solubility limit of 2.8 ppm.

The assumption that the diffusion coefficient is independent of concentration means that the adsorption on the sea sediments is directly proportional to the concentration of the elements in the liquid. We can then write

$$D = D_s/\theta^2 \quad 1/(1+((1-\epsilon)/\epsilon) \quad \rho_s Kd) \qquad (5.8)$$

where D_s is the diffusion in the sea water, θ^2 a global tortuosity factor. As the value of D_s /12/ and θ^2 /13/ can be found in the literature, from the evaluation of D it is possible also to calculate the Kd value.

In Table 5.4 are given the effective diffusion coefficients of some elements and the values of the Kd coefficients calculated following Eq. (5.8). It can be seen that the diffusion coefficient decreases regularly with the increase of the ion valencies.

TABLE 5.4.

Element	$D\ (cm^2/s)$	Boundary condition	Kd cm^3/gr
Cs^+	6.0×10^{-7}	ϕ const	13
$(UO2)^{2+}$	5.0×10^{-8}	C_o const	35
Co^{2+}	1.7×10^{-8}	ϕ const	170
Sm^{3+}	3.7×10^{-10}	ϕ const	6800
Ce^{3+}	3.6×10^{-10}	ϕ const	7000

For cesium the initial assumption that the diffusion is independent from concentration can be questionable. As a matter of fact, studies /14/ on adsorption of cesium on sea sediments show that the adsorption coefficient decreases strongly with the increase of the concentration in the liquid. In fact, it has been noted that the test at 21 days, when cesium concentration is rather low, shows a lower diffusion coefficient. However, for the other tests the diffusion coefficients obtained do not differe significantly. In Table 5.4 is reported such a value which has to be considered typical of a high concentration of cesium.

A similar analysis has been performed on the diffusion of elements in sediments charged with corrosion products.

The normal content of iron in the sediments is around 2%. The corrosion of mild steel has introduced in the sediments an additional content of iron which can reach a maximum value of 5%.

Two elements have been taken into consideration; uranium and cobalt. While for Co the diffusion coefficient is practically unaffected, for U the maximum iron content causes a decrease even of an order of magnitude. It seems reasonable to assume that such a decrease is due to the variation of the redox conditions which influence the speciation of the uranium. More data are needed to confirm this point.

5.5 Surface Extension Due to Glass Fracture

Large-scale glass castings have to be cooled extremely slowly if fracturing is to be avoided and such slow rates may not be possible in a production schedule. In addition, Hall /15/ has shown that the radioactive self-heat of the glass introduces a term into the equation used for calculating the stress leading to fracture that is effectively equivalent to a faster cooling rate. Thus cooling the real glass blocks extremely slowly will not be sufficient to prevent cracking.

The most complete study of the cracking produced at various cooling rates has been made by Peters and Slate /16/. They showed that the extra surface area produced by the cracking decreased with the cooling rate as shown in Figure 5.8. A cooling schedule lasting as long as 20 days was required to eliminate cracking in the 60 cm diameter inactive cylinders they used. However, as noted above, active cylinders would still crack, even after this treatment. Empirical results of similar fracture studies by Smith and Baxter /17/ suggested that to prevent bulk cracking, the temperature gradients in the glass must not exceed ca. 1°C/cm.

French workers /17/ simulated the temperature histories of glass blocks in various management scenarios (water decontamination after various times, air cooled storage, etc.) and found increases in surface area of the glass compared to monolithic blocks of factors between 9 and 16.6.

Much of the cracking in the glass occurs near the glass/canister interface due to thermal expansion mis-match. This can be ameliorated /17/:

a) by using carbon steel canisters (expansion coefficient $\alpha = 11-14 \times 10^{-6}$ °C^{-1}) rather than those of austenitic stainless steel ($\alpha = 17-20 \times 10^{-6}$ °C^{-1});

b) by coating the canister with graphite, which prevents the glass from sticking to the steel;

c) by using a liner to the canister such as alumina-silica papers, or coatings of this material applied directly to the canister walls.

The effect of this fracturing on the release of radionuclides from the glass has not been thoroughly investigated. The simplest and most pessimistic assumption is to assume that all the extra surface area produced by the cracks is freely available to the leachant. If this if done, release rates are very high to start with, as the many fine particles produced are dissolved. Later, the release rates decrease somewhat but still remain well above those calculated for a monolithic block.

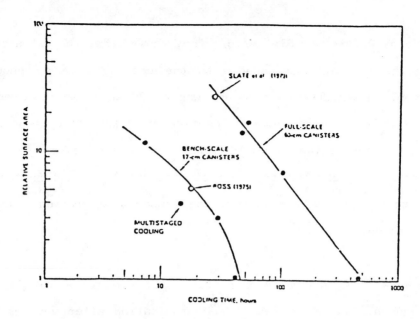

FIGURE 5.8.   Effect of cooling time on relative surface area of thermal
cracks in 17 cm and 60 cm dia canisters.

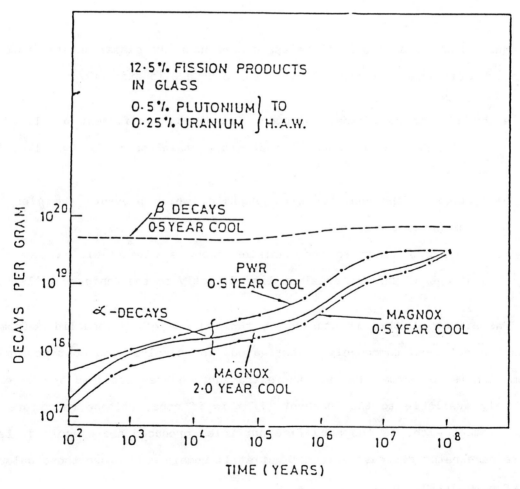

FIGURE 5.9.   The number of decays per gram as a function of time for highly active
vitrified waste. The different curves refer to different reactors and
processing conditions as indicated.

However, Perez and Westsik /19/ investigated the effective leaching from cracks using a static test at 90°C. They clamped glass pellets together with various thicknesses of spacer between them to simulate different crack width. They found that leaching from cracks with 0.38 mm widths were 2-5 times less than leaching from external surfaces, whilst no apparent leaching was observed from cracks with nominally zero widths. Thus, in a repository, as long as the cracks in the glass are held closed by either the remains of the canister or by the sediments, they will probably not contribute to the release of radioisotopes.

5.6 Radiation Effects

We will consider firstly the effects on the leach rate of radiation damage that occurs prior to the attack by water. The cumulative numbers of α and β decays received by the glass are given in Figure 5.9 /20/.

Note that almost all the β-decays occur within the first 100 years. The number of α-decays in the glass increases slightly if the fuel is stored before stored before reprocessing because of the decay of ^{241}Pu, which is removed by reprocessing, to ^{241}Am which is not. The higher values for PWR compared to Magnox waste are because of higher burn-up of the former (30,000 MWD/te vs 3,000 MWD/te) which leads to a greater accumulation of the higher actinides. In contrast to the β-decays, the cumulative total of α-decays continues to increase for millions of years. Estimates of the numbers of various events in the glass in the first 100 years, the range of the particles, and the number of displacements produced, are given in Table 5.5 /20,21/. It is assumed that damage to the glass only occurs because of displacement of atoms from their original positions. This occurs largely by collisions for α-particles and the recoil nuclei from α-decay. The values in column 4 of Table 5.5 were calculated assuming 25 eV per displacement. There is some work /20/ that suggests that ionisa-

TABLE 5.5. BASIC DATA FOR RADIATION DAMAGE IN VITRIFIED WASTE. THE RANGE OF VALUES DOES NOT REFLECT UNCERTAINTIES IN THE CALCULATIONS, BUT REPRESENTS VARIATIONS IN REACTOR TYPE AND PROCESSING TIMES.

Radiation	Decay cm^{-3} in first 100 y	Approximate range of particle	Collision damage		Ionization events	
			Displacements per decay	Displacements cm^{-3} in first 100 y	Deposital energy in first 100 y (rads)*	Displacements cm^{-3} in first 100 y**
Alpha	$3 \times 10^{17} - 1.5 \times 10^{19}$	α : 20 μm recoil: 30 mm	180 1200	$4 \times 10^{20} - 2 \times 10^{22}$	$10^{10} - 5 \times 10^{11}$	$3 \times 10^{19} - 1.5 \times 10^{21}$
Beta	$2 \times 10^{19} - 1 \times 10^{20}$	1 mm	~ 1	$2 \times 10^{19} - 1 \times 10^{20}$	$6 \times 10^{10} - 3 \times 10^{11}$	$2 \times 10^{20} - 10^{21}$
Gamma	similar to beta	~ cms	≪1	–	$10^{11} - 10^{12}$	$3 \times 10^{20} - 1 \times 10^{21}$
$10_B(n,\alpha)^7Li$	4×10^{10}	^7Li : 5 μm Li: 3 μm	110 180	1.2×10^{13}	10^3	3×10^{12}
Fissions: spontaneous induced	$2 \times 10^{10} - 2 \times 10^{12}$ 10^{11}	~ 10 μm	~ 4×10^5	$5 \times 10^{16} - 8 \times 10^{17}$	$10^5 - 10^6$	$3 \times 10^{14} - 3 \times 10^{15}$
Neutrons: from (α, n) from fission	$1.5 \times 10^{12} - 7 \times 10^{13}$ $10^{11} - 3 \times 10^{12}$	~ 100 cm	~ 10^3	$10^{15} - 10^{17}$	$10^3 - 10^5$ (in secondary cascades)	$3 \times 10^{12} - 3 \times 10^{14}$

* 1 rad = 100 ergs g^{-1} = 1.6×10^{14} eV cm^{-3} in glass of density 2.6 g cm^{-3}.

** Assuming: 6×10^4 eV per displacement.

tion effects can lead to structural damage but with a very low efficiency in terms of damage per unit deposited energy, e.g. electron irradiation can lead to the compaction of fused silica. However, it has not been established experimentally that this mechanism occurs in any of the vitreous waste forms.

If only collision damage occurs, the dominant damaging events will be the recoil nuclei from α-decay. The damage caused by the recoil nuclei is very dense within the track of the recoiling nucleus since ca. 1200 displacements are produced within a volume of about 10 nm^3, i.e. about 10^{21} displacements cm^{-3}; the glass contains about 7×10^{22} atoms cm^{-3}. Thus, each decay produces a small region of glass which is heavily damaged more or less to saturation. Once these small damaged regions touch and overlap, the whole material becomes saturated from a radiation damage point of view.

If there is a component of damage from ionising events, the electrons and gamma rays could play an important role, especially during the first 100 years, when these effects could outweigh the results of α-decay. However, the character of the damage will be different with the displacements spread throughout the material. A single 0.5 MeV electron may produce 10-100 displacements spread along its range of ca. 1 mm. It is thus of paramount importance to test the stability of the glass to α-decays and of secondary importance to test their stability to β-decays.

In experiments /20/ to test the stability of glasses to β-decays, samples were irradiated with 0.5 MeV electrons to a fluence of 10^{19} electrons cm^{-3}. The results are given in Table 5.6 where it can be seen that the leach rate changes by less than a fator of two after this irradiation.

Most simulations have been carried out by incorporating a few percent of a relatively short-lived α-emitting isotope (e.g. ^{244}Cm or ^{238}Pu) in glasses of the same composition as those considered for practical use. Provided the iso-

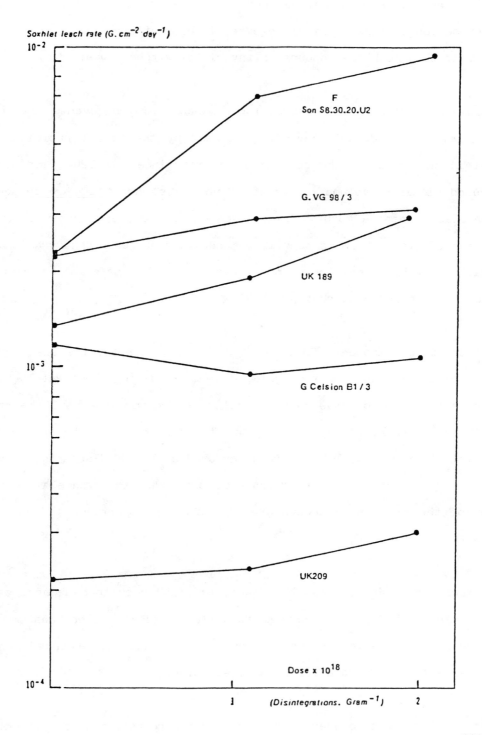

FIGURE 5.10.   Leach rates of five glass compositions doped with ^{238}PuO plotted against dose.

TABLE 5.6. LEACH RATES (SOXHLET TEST) FOR GLASSES BEFORE AND AFTER IRRADIATION WITH 0.5 MeV ELECTRONS TO A DOSE OF 10^{19} e cm^{-2}. EACH IRRADIATION TOOK 10 DAYS AT MEAN BEAM CURRENT OF ca. 2 μ A cm^{-2}.

Irradiation temperature (°C)	Glass composition	Leach rate (mg cm^{-2} day^{-1})	
		Normal	Irradiated
125 – 130	210	1.4	1.9
25 – 50	189	1.3	2.5
	Crystallised*	1.5	2.6
	209	0.26	0.36
	Crystallised*	0.36	0.34

* 100 days at 700°C.

tope is uniformly distributed in solid solution, these tests subject the glass to exactly the same processes that will occur in practice, albeit at a higher dose rate by a factor of 10^4 - 10^5. Table 5.7 shows the results of tests at Harwell on UK glass 189 doped with 5.07 wt% $^{238}PoO_2$. It can be seen that the leach rate has changed by ongly a factor of 2 after a dose of 5.6×10^{18} α-decays per gram. It is, however, possible that not all the 238PuO_2 is in solid solution, since some indications of inhomogeneity were observed in autoradiographs. To avoid this problem, samples of various European glass compositions were doped with only 2.5 wt% $^{238}PuO_2$ /22/. These too showed only small increases in leach rate with dose, as shown in Figure 5.10: the same samples were used at each dose level after repolishing to avoid sample to sample variations in leach rate.

Some results on glasses doped with ^{244}Cm are shown in Table 5.8. None of the accumulated doses goes above 10^{18} decays g^{-1}, but again it is clear that only small increases in leach rate occur.

Dran et al. /27,28/ irradiated glasses and crystalline minerals with a beam of 200 keV Pb ions and showed that an enhanced leach rate occurred above a critical dose of about 5×10^{12} ions cm^{-2} which corresponded to the dose at

TABLE 5.7. LEACH TESTS ON SAMPLES OF GLASS 189 DOPED WITH $^{238}\text{PuO}_2$. THE EQUIVA-
LENT TIMES ASSUME 0.5% OF THE PLUTONIUM AND 0.25% OF THE URANIUM
ORIGINALLY PRESENT IN MAGNOX FUEL GO INTO THE WASTE. THE FUEL IS
ASSUMED TO BE REPROCESSED AFTER 6 MONTHS OUT OF THE REACTOR. THE
EFFECT OF THE BETA DECAYS IS ASSUMED TO BE NEGLIGIBLE. THE INITIAL
SOXHLET LEACH RATE EXPECTED FOR UNDOPED GLASS OF THIS COMPOSITION
IS 1.3 ± 0.2 mg cm^{-2} day^{-1}.

| | | | Holding temperature | |
| | | First year | 50°C | 170°C |
		Subsequent year	20°C	20°C
Date	Dose (α-disintegrations per gram)	Equivalent time (years)	Leach rates mg cm	day
Nov. 1975	0.89×10^{18}	7,000	1.6	1.5
Feb. 1977	2.0×10^{18}	250,000	2.3	2.3
Mar. 1977	2.1×10^{18}	300,000	2.4	2.2
Nov. 1977	2.7×10^{18}	500,000	2.3	2.6
July 1978	3.3×10^{18}	700,000	2.3	2.5
Jan. 1981	5.5×10^{18}	1.4 M	3.2	2.7
Feb. 1981	5.6×10^{18}		3.0	

which the zones damaged by each Pb ion overlapped; the zones had a diameter of about 100 Å, and a length of 500 Å. Each incident Pb ion produced about 3000 displacements so that the critical dose is $3 \times 10^{21}/1380 = 2.2 \times 10^{18}$ α-decays cm^{-3}, equivalent to 8.5×10^{17} α-decays·g^{-1}. The increased leach rates observed after this critical dose varied from zero to a factor of about 50 depending on composition, with most of the increases being between X15 and X30. The leach rates were normally measured at 100°C in a 250 ℓ$^{-1}$ NaCl solution.

Since none of the experiments with doped glasses showed any similar effects, even at doses considerably exceeding Dran's threshold dose, some explanation was needed of the difference between the two sets of results. In order

TABLE 5.8. LEACH TESTS ON GLASSES DOPED WITH ^{244}Cm.

Material and reference	Leach method**	Parameter measured	Initial leach rate (g cm^{-2}day^{-1}) LR_O	Dose (D) α-decays g^{-1}	Final leach rate (g cm^{-2}day^{-1}) LR_D	Radio LR_D/LR_O
PNL glass 77-260 (vitreous) /23/	Soxhlet	Wt. loss	3.2×10^{-4}	1.4×10^{18}	2.8×10^{-4}	0.9
		Cm in leachate	9.0×10^{-7}	1.4×10^{18}	8.0×10^{-7}	0.9
	Static, pH 9	Wt. loss	8.0×10^{-5}	1.4×10^{18}	9.0×10^{-6}	0.1
	Static, pH 4	Wt. loss	1.2×10^{-4}	1.4×10^{18}	0.8×10^{-4}	0.7
PNL glass 77-260 (crystallised) /23/	Soxhlet	Wt. loss	1.8×10^{-4}	1.4×10^{18}	1.3×10^{-4}	0.7
		Cm in leachate	3.8×10^{-6}	1.4×10^{18}	1.2×10^{-6}	0.3
	Static, pH 9	Wt. loss	1.8×10^{-5}	1.4×10^{18}	0.7×10^{-4}	4.0
	Static, pH 4	Wt. loss	2.0×10^{-4}	1.4×10^{18}	2.3×10^{-4}	1.1
PNL glass 72-68 /24/	Static	K in leachate	$6.0 \times 10^{-6*}$	8.3×10^{17}	$1.1 \times 10^{-5*}$	1.8
		Cm in leachate	$(7 \times 10^{-8})+$	8.3×10^{17}	1.0×10^{-7}	1.4
SRL glass SRP /25/	Static	Cm in leachate	1.6×10^{-9}	3.7×10^{17}	$(5.6+3.0) \times 10^{-9++}$	3.5+1.5
VG 98/3 /26/	Static	Cm in leachate	5×10^{-7}	1.4×10^{18}	5×10^{-7}	1.0

* Values on doped and undoped samples compared. Initial values of doped samples not given.

+ Value at 5.3×10^{17} alpha decays g^{-1}. Initial value not given.

++ Average and standard deviation of 5 readings.

** In the "static method" the water was changed (daily af first, less frequent later) and analysed where an element is mentioned.

to check that the choice of leachant was not the cause, one of the samples doped with 5 wt% $^{238}PuO_2$ was also leached in a 250 g·ℓ^{-1} NaCl solution, but again showed only a small increase in leach rate (Table 5.9). Note that the leach rate in distilled water is an order of magnitude less than that in a Soxhlet test and that in NaCl solution it is an order of magnitude lower still.

TABLE 5.9. LEACH TESTS AT 100°C ON GLASS 189 IN NaCl SOLUTION. THE RESULTS ON THE IRRADIATED SAMPLE WERE OBTAINED AFTER A DOSE OF 5.5×10^{18} DISINTEGRATIONS PER GRAM. THE NaCl concentration was 250 g·ℓ^{-1}. ALTHOUGH THE CONDITIONS ARE DESCRIBED AS STATIC, THERE WOULD BE CONSIDERABLE CONVECTIVE STIRRING.

Sample	Leaching conditions	Leach rate (g·$cm^{-2}d^{-1}$)
Irradiated	Soxhlet	2.7×10^{-3}
Control	Static distilled water	2.7×10^{-4}
Control	Static NaCl solution	3.1×10^{-5}
Irradiated	Static NaCl solution	3.7×10^{-5}

A possible explanation is that the enhanced leach rate is caused by surface cracking, since glasses do expand or contract under irradiation /32/ and the ions used by Dran penetrate only about 500 Å into the glass. The effect was illustrated /27/ by irradiating through a grid and, after leaching, the irradiated areas were shown to be depressed below the level of the unirradiated ones. The dividing lines were very sharp and it is not easy to reconcile this with spalling, although not impossible if the irradiated areas had contracted.

An alternative explanation is that some relaxation occurs in the simulations with α-emitters (and by implication would also occur in the real case) that does not occur in the bombardment experiments because of the greatly reduced time scale /20/.

In addition to the relatively small effects of radiation damage to the glass, discussed in Section 2.3 above, we must also consider the possible effects that radiolysis of the leachant might have on the leach rate. This is a complex topic because not only do α- and γ-radiations produce different ions in the water, but the situation is critically dependent on whether nitrogen is present, since this can lead to production of nitric acid. The subject has recently been reviewed by Burns et al. /20,29/. The dose rates to the leachant are given for various times in Table 5.10. From this table it is clear that the radiolysis will be particularly important in the case of an accident which destroys the protection given by the canister during the thermal period.

TABLE 5.10. TYPICAL RADIATION DOSE RATES TO THE LEACHANT IN A WASTE REPOSITORY.

Time after vitrification (years)	Dose rates (Mrad. hr^{-1})	
	β / γ	α
4	0.53	0.027
50	0.08	0.023
500	ca. 0	0.011

McVay and Pederson /30/ first leached samples of glass 76-68 at 50°C in a gamma flux of ca. 2 $Mrad \cdot h^{-1}$, which is about ten times the maximum that will occur in practice. Release rates increased by a factor that varies slightly from element to element but were generally ca. X5 and did not depend very much on whether air was excluded. If air was present the pH was sharply reduced, but the only significant increase in release rate was for iron. Later experiments /31/ suggested that in the absence of air the increase in release rate was less at higher temperatures, decreasing in one series of experiments from 168% at 50°C to zero at 90°C. This is consistent with the experiments of Marples et al. /32/ who found no increase in leach rate at 90°C when the leachant was irradiated with X-rays at about the same dose rate. The surface dose rate of the

238
Pu-doped samples described in Section 2.3 is about 4 Mrad.h^{-1} of α-radiation and this perfore must irradiate the leachant/sample interface. As noted above, only small effects on the leach rate are observed and these are attributed to damage to the specimen, not to radiolysis. Radiolysis effects must be small since the initial leach rate is similar to that of the undoped specimens /32/. It should be noted, however, that these experiments were carried out at 100°C. One of the few experiments, carried out at lower temperatures (25°C) where the data for actinide doped and undoped samples could be compared, was reported by Mendel et al. /33/. In their static test, the potassium leach rate of Cm-doped 72-68 was about twice that of the undoped glass, up to 140 days. Here the surface α-dose rate would have been ca. 20 Mrad.h^{-1}. No attempt was apparently made to exclude air from the system.

It has to be noted that in the presence of air or nitrogen, nitric acid is produced by irradiation and this might cause an increase in leach rate. However, a seabed repository should be free of air pockets and the absence of air as a separate phase precludes the formation of nitric acid because this compound is a negligible product of the irradiation of water containing dissolved nitrogen.

5.7 Conclusions

Due to the limited amount of specific tests it is rather difficult to draw precise conclusions. We will try to list some preliminary points.

- Static tests conducted in sea water have shown that after an initial period of fast linear corrosion, the attack slows down noticeably. It seems probable that in this second period the glass leaching depends on a silica concentration which is controlled by the reprecipitation of an alumino-magnesium silicate.

- Tests in sediments for the period investigated show only the linear part. It appears that the absorptive properties of the sediments do not allow to reach such a concentration of silica which gives rise to saturation effects.

- It seems probable that for longer times, when the absorptive sites are saturated, even in sediments, lower leaching rates will be encountered. However, lacking the experimental evidence, it seems advisable to be conservative and assume that even for long periods of time the degradation rate continues to be linear.

- No tests have been performed with different types of sediment. In particular it has not been possible to use the specific sediments which have been extracted at depths higher than 30 m.

- Due to the litostatic pressure of 30 m of sediments it appears reasonable to assume that internal surfaces of the glass blocks do not contribute substantially to the release of radionuclides. Once again, however, no specific tests have been conducted.

- The influence of the radiation damage of the glass, of the radiolysis of the interstitial sea water, of the water pressure does not appear to be large. Probably the effect of all these phenomena does not go beyond the degree of the uncertainty of the data assumed.

References

/1/ Lanza, F., Ronsecco, C. (1986). Corrosion of low carbon steel in clay and sea sediments. EUR 10522 EN.

/2/ Marples, J.A.C. (1985). Factors affecting the leachability of vitrified waste. S.P. I.07.C2.85.50, December 1985).

/3/ Hebel, W., Bruggeman, A., Donato, A., Furrer, J. and White, I.F. (1985). Management of nuclear airborne wastes and tritium retention. In Proc. of the 2nd Eur. Conf. on Radioactive Waste Management and Disposal, Cambridge University Press.

/4/ Whitmell, D.S., Geens, L., Penzhorn, R.D. and Smith, M.J.S., Capture and immobilization of Kripton 95. Ibidem.

/5/ Lanza, F., Parnisari, E. and Pietra, R., Evaluation of the leaching of a borosilicate glass and of the corresponding release of various elements in sea sediments. To be published in the S.P. series.

/6/ Seabed Disposal of High Level Radioactive Waste, NEA, Paris 1984.

/7/ Kuhn, W.L., Peters, R.D., Simonson, S.A. (1983). Development of a leach model for a commercial nuclear waste glass. Nucl. Tech. 62, pp 82-89, (October 1983).

/8/ Thomassin, J.H. (1984). Thèse de Doctorat, Université d'Orléans.

/9/ Conradt, R., Roggendort, H., Scholze, H. (1983). Chemical durability of a multicomponent glass in a simulated carnallite/rock salt environment. Proc. of the Scientific Basis for Nuclear Waste Management, North Holland.

/10/ Carlaw, H.S., Jaegger, J.C.J. (1959). Conduction of heat in solids. P. 75 Clarendon Press.

/11/ Crank, J. (1983). The mathematics of diffusion. p. 20, Clarendon Press.

/12/ Yuan-Hui Li, Gregory, S. (1974). Diffusion of ions in sea water and in deep sea sediments. Geochim. and Cosmochim. Acta, 38, pp. 703-714.

/13/ Ullman, W.J., Aller, R.C. (1982). Diffusion coefficients in nearshore marine sediments. Limnol. Oceanogr. 27(3), pp. 552-556.

/14/ Erickson, K.L. (1979). Radionuclide sorption studies on abyssal red clays. Radioactive Waste in Geologic Storate, S. Fried (ed.), Am. Chemic. Soc., Washington D.C.

/15/ Hall, A.R. (1982). Private communication.

/16/ Peters, R.D. and Slate, S.C. (1981). Fracturing of simulated high level waste glass in canisters. Nuclear Engineering and Design, 67, p. 425; and Battelle Pacific Northwest Laboratories Report PNL 3948 (1981).

/17/ Smith, P.K. and Baxter, C.A. (1981). <u>Fracture during cooling of cast borosilicate glass containing nuclear wastes</u>. Du Pont, Savannah River, Report No. DP-1602.

/18/ Laude, F., Vernaz, E. and Saint Gaudens, M. (1982). <u>Fracture during cooling of cast borosilicate glass containing nuclear wastes</u>. Scientific Basis for Radioactive Waste Management, V.W. Lutze (ed.), North Holland, p. 239.

/19/ Perez, J.M. and Westsik, J.H. (1981). <u>Effects of cracks on glass leaching</u>. Nuclear and Chemical Waste Management, 2, p. 165.

/20/ Burns, W.G., Hughes, A.E., Marples, J.A.C., Nelson, R.S. and Stoneham, A.M. (1982). <u>Effects of radiation on the leach rates of vitrified radioactive waste</u>. UKAEA Harwell Report, AERE-R 10189 9 (1981) and J. Nuclear Materials, 107 (1982) p. 245.

/21/ Boult, K.A., Dalton, J.T., Hall, A.R., Hough, A. and Marples, J.A.C. (1979). <u>The leaching of radioactive waste storage glasses</u>. AERE Harwell, UK Report AERE-R 9188 and in "Ceramics in Nuclear Waste Management", T.D. Chikalla and J.E. Mendel (eds.), American Ceramics Soc. Symposium, Cincinnati, p. 248, CONF 790420.

/22/ De Batist, R. et al. (1983). <u>Testing and evaluation of solidified high level waste forms</u>. Commission of the European Communities Report EUR 8424 EN.

/23/ Weber, W.J., Turcotte, R.P., Bunnell, L.R., Roberts, F.P. and Westsik, J.W. (1979). <u>Radiation effects in vitreous and devitrified simulated waste glass</u>. Ceramics in Nuclear Waste Management, T.D. Chikalla and J.E. Mendel (eds.), CONF-790420, p. 294.

/24/ Mendel, J.E., Ross, W.A., Roberts, F.P., Turcotte, R.P., Katayama, Y.B. and Westsik, J.H. (1976). <u>Thermal and radiation effects on borosilicate waste glasses</u>. Management of Radioactive Wastes from the Nuclear Fuel Cycle (IAEA Vienna), Vol. II, 49.

/25/ Bibler, N.E. and Kelley, J.A., <u>Effect of internal alpha radiation on borosilicate glass containing Savannah River plant waste</u>. Dupont (Savannah River) Report DP-1482.

/26/ Scheffler, K. and Riege, U. (1977). <u>Investigations on the long term radiation stability of borosilicate glass against alpha emitters</u>. Kernforschungszentrum Karlsruhe Report KfK 2422.

/27/ Dran, J.C., Maurette, M. and Petit, J.C. (1980). <u>Radioactive waste storage materials: their -recoil aging</u>. Science, 209, p. 1518.

/28/ Dran, J.C., Maurette, M. Petit, J.C. and Vassent, B. (1981). Radiation damage effects on the leach resistance of glasses and minerals: implications for radioactive waste storage. Scientific Basis for Nuclear Waste Management, 3, J.G. Moore (ed.), Plenum Press, p. 449.

/29/ Burns, W.G. et al. (1982). Radiation effects and the leach rates of vitrified radioactive waste. Nature, 295, p. 130.

/30/ McVay, G.L.M. and Pederson, L.R. (1981). Effect of gamma radiation on glass leaching. J. Amer, Ceram. Soc., 64, p. 154.

/31/ McVay, G.L. (1981). Personal communication.

/32/ Marples, J.A.C. et al. (1981). Testing and evaluation of the properties of various potential materials for immobilizing high activity waste. European Applied Research Reports, 3(3), p. 395, and Commission of the European Community Report EUR 7138 EN.

/33/ Mendel, J.E. et al. (1977). Annual report on the characteristics of high level waste glasses. Battelle Pacific Northwest Laboratories Report BNWL-2252.

CHAPTER 6: SEA WATER-SEDIMENT INTERACTION

6.1 <u>Introduction</u>

Sub-seabed disposal of high level radioactive waste within marine pelagic sediment is currently receiving considerable attention as an alternative to onland disposal options /1/. Marine sediments are characterized by several properties that would enhance waste isolation. These include high plasticity, low permeability, and high adsorptive capacity /2,3/.

Feasibility assessment of sub-seabed disposal necessitates modelling the chemical reactivity of the sediment-sea water system and characterizing diffusional transport processes, both for near field and far field environments.

The near field is the sediment envelope in the immediate vicinity of a buried canister. Correspondingly, the near field can be subjected to relatively high temperatures, perhaps as great as 300°C. Thus, the near field-far field transition will be characterized by a large thermal gradient.

The chapter is disseminated into several portions each of which emphasizes specific key components relevant to experimental design and acquisition of experimental data pertinent to the assessment of the feasibility of sub-seabed disposal of high level radioactive waste.

Part I of this chapter reviews requisite techniques and procedures needed to perform and gather data successfully from experiments at constant temperature and pressure and in a thermal gradient. These techniques are applied to various chemical systems, and this constitutes the remainder of the report. For example, Part II describes results of experiments at constant temperature (200-300°C) and constant pressure (500 bars). These experiments were designed to evaluate mineral stability and alteration processes in sea water at elevated temperatures and pressures. Part III describes results of experiments designed to model the effect of a thermal gradient on mass transport processes. These experiments have successfully characterized temperature and pressure dependent sediment-sea water interaction and have established, for the first time, Soret coefficients for pertinent aqueous species at temperatures and pressures consistent with the near field environment associated with sub-seabed disposal of high level radioactive waste.

6.2 Experimental Apparatus

Constant Temperature-Hydrothermal-Solution Equipment

Constant temperature, hydrothermal experiments reviewed as part of this report (Part II) were performed using Dickson hydrothermal apparatus /4/ with modifications by Seyfried et al. /5/. This apparatus (Figure 6.1) consists of a gold reaction cell enclosed in a pressure vessel (American Instrument Co., Silver Springs, Maryland) and electric furnace. The furnace temperature is maintained within ± 2°C by a proportioning controller. The reaction cell is seabed with a titanium top and solution samples are obtained through an internal gold filter and a titanium exit tube by opening a sampling valve. Constant hydrostatic pressure is maintained while sampling by pumping water into the pressure vessel around the reaction cell. The assembly is mounted on a rack and continuously rocked through 180°C at 20 times per minute. Reaction kinetics are thus accelerated by suspending the sediment in sea water to insure a maximum surface of reaction.

Sampling of the aqueous fluid can be accomplished at constant temperature and pressure at any time during the experiment. Quench fluid and reacted sediment is also obtained at the end of each experiment.

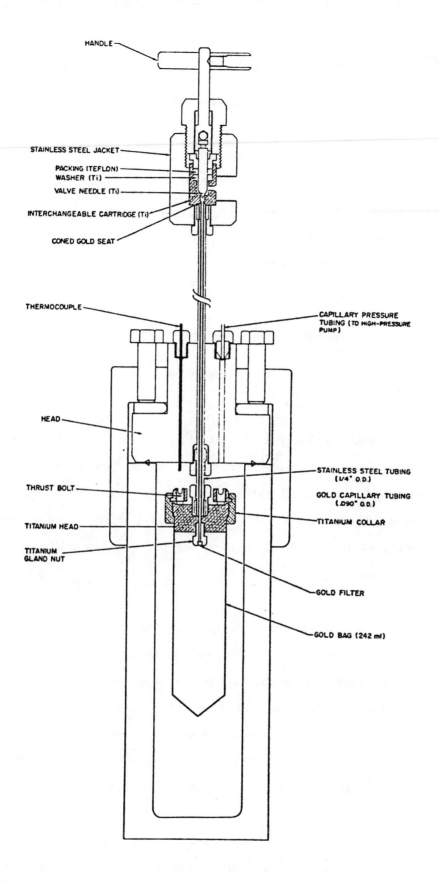

FIGURE 6.1. Schematic diagram of Dickson Hydrothermal Apparatus.

Thermal Gradient Equipment

The reaction cell employed for thermal gradient experiments (Part II - this report) consists of a steel pressure vessel with a titanium liner (Figure 6.2).   Sampling valves are secured to each end of the cell to permit sampling of "hot" and "cool" zones. A hollow titanium plug packed with titanium filings positioned at the bottom of the cell serves to filter fluids extracted from the "hot" zone and to facilitate removal of reacted solid products at the end of the experiment.

6.3 Constant Temperature-Pressure Experiments

Introduction

As noted previously the purpose of this portion of the present report is to elucidate the effects of temperature, sea water chemistry, sediment chemistry and mineralogy on chemical exchange, secondary mineral formation, and reacted fluid chemistry, especially pH and fO_2. pH and fO_2 are master variables, and are of critical importance to alteration processes and the entire sub-seabed disposal concept.

Results reviewed here are from experiments conducted in Dickson Hydrothermal Apparatus at 200°C and 300°C and 500 bars pressure utilizing sediment of various redox states to understand better how this important parameter may affect near field geochemistry. All experiments were performed at sea water/sediment ratios of 5 and for several thousand hours. Copenhagen standard sea water was utilized for all experiments. Sediment and sea water were loaded into the gold reaction cell under a N_2 atmosphere to avoid oxidation by air of sediment components.

Periodically, during the experiments solution was removed from within the

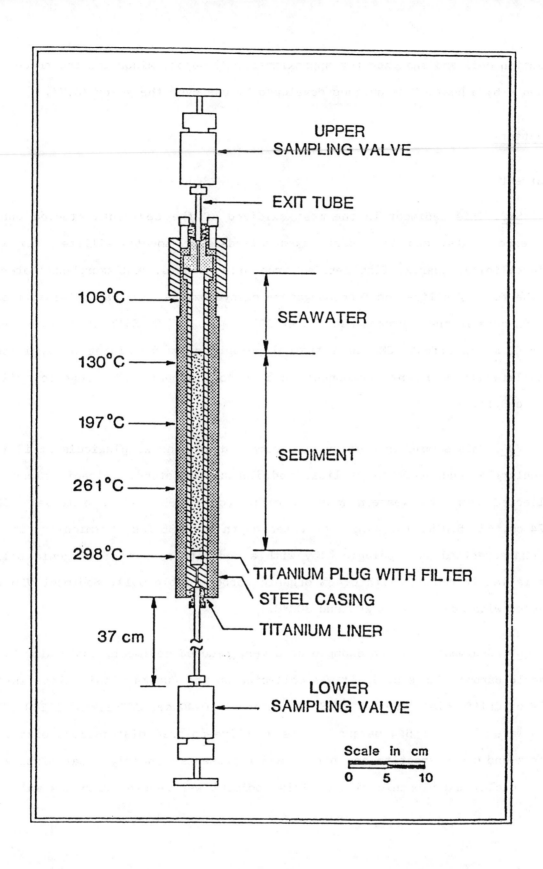

FIGURE 6.2. Schematic diagram of temperature gradient reaction
cell. <u>In situ</u> temperatures maintained throughout
the gradient experiments are indicated.

reaction cell and analyzed for approximately 20 major, minor and the trace components by a host of techniques developed by use over the years /6,7/.

Reactants

Sediment

SM2. This sediment is the most oxidized of the sediments studied during our experiments, and is a dark brown mixed-layer smectile-illite clay with clinoptiloite, quartz, fish debris, iron oxide crusts, and amorphous material in the form of silica and ferromanganese oxyhydroxides. SM2 was obtained from a piston core in the northern Pacific at 30°20.9'N, 157°50.85'W at a water depth of 5800 m. In effect, SM2 is a typical pelagic clay containing a significant metalliferous sediment component and minor amount of biogenic silica (Table 6.1).

V36. This sample is a silty clay composed of quartz, plagioclase, illite, Fe-chlorite, and amorphous silica, radiolarians, diatoms, volcanic glass /3/ collected from the western North Pacific (core V36/12-43P, interval 1025-1174 cm, 33°45.0'N, 151°45.8E) at water depth of 3185 fms. Chemically, it may be characterized as a pelagic clay with a moderate amount of biogenic silica and is fairly reduced with 0.43% organic carbon (Table 6.1). Sediment V36 was reacted with sea water at 200 and 300°C.

CD. Sediment CD is an example of a very reduced sediment, containing 3.99% organic carbon (Table 6.1). It was collected on the Guaymas Basin slope in the Gulf of California (core BAV 79-E-10, interval 10-40 cm, 27°52.2'N, 111°93.7'W) at a water depth of 644 meters. It is an olive-colored diatomaceous ooze with quartz and minor smectite and barite and represents a nearly equal mixture of pelagic clay and biogenic silica. This sediment was reacted with sea water at 300°C.

TABLE 6.1. CHEMICAL ANALYSIS OF SEDIMENTS UTILIZED IN STUDY. SAMPLES WERE WASHED AND DRIED AT 40°C.

Percent	SM2	V36	CD
SiO_2	51.77	58.31	64.39
Al_2O_3	13.37	14.79	8.01
$(Fe_2O_3)_T$	9.09	6.52	2.70
MgO	3.49	2.79	1.81
CaO	1.29	2.17	1.68
Na_2O	0.79	1.79	0.72
K_2O	3.71	2.63	1.48
MnO	1.30	0.21	0.02
TiO_2	0.59	0.80	0.33
P_2O_5	0.49	0.10	0.20
H_2O	0.94	0.82	1.08
H_2O^+	12.15	6.87	16.96
Total	98.98	97.70	99.38
C_{inorg}	0.007	0.000	–
C_{org}	0.064	0.43	3.99
ppm			
Ba	381	681	519
Co	45	27	5
Cr	43	79	49
Cu	276	112	29
Ni	152	47	35
Pb	42	28	34
Sr	203	159	145
Zn	165	101	75

Results

Solution Chemistry

<u>Mg, Ca, Na, K, Cl, SO_4 and pH.</u> The major element chemistry of sea water was significantly modified during all of the experiments performed (Figure 6.4). In general, sea water lost Mg and SO_4 and gained K. The pH fell to a minimum during the first several days of each experiment but rose subsequentl as the concentration of Mg became depleted in the fluid. Ca displayed a tendency to decrease as pH fell but increased again as pH rose. Na appears to have behaved in a manner similar to Ca when the Na concentrations are normalized to a constant sea water chlorinity of 19375 ppm. Chloride generally increased slightly during the course of the experiments due to water uptake by hydrated alteration products.

<u>SiO_2.</u> The concentration of silica in solution appears to have been controlled primarily by the solubility of amorphous silica in the form of organic siliceous ooze. Thus, SiO_2 reached concentrations of 600 to 900 ppm at 200°C and 1500 to 2000 ppm at 300°C. SiO_2 fell to slightly less than 1250 ppm in the experiment with sediment SM2 after 1347 hours, apparently due to the depletion of amorphous silica.

<u>Mn.</u> Mn exists primarily as Mn(IV) (e.g., MnO_2) in sediment SM2 and acts as the principal oxidizing agent in that sediment (Figure 6.4). Thus, the Mn concentration of 700 to 800 ppm in the SM2 experiment at 300°C reflects the reduction of Mn(IV) to Mn(II) through the oxidation of organic matter and ferrous iron in the sediment. That MnO_2 is present in an amount in excess of the reducing agents and thus maintained oxidizing conditions during the experiment is demonstrated by Au concentrations of 1.7 to 1.8 ppm (see Discussion). Mn concentrations were less than 100 ppm in the experiments involving the reduced sediments V36 and CD due to the small amount of MnO_2 originally present in them. The reduced nature of these experiments is further demonstrated by the low Au concentrations.

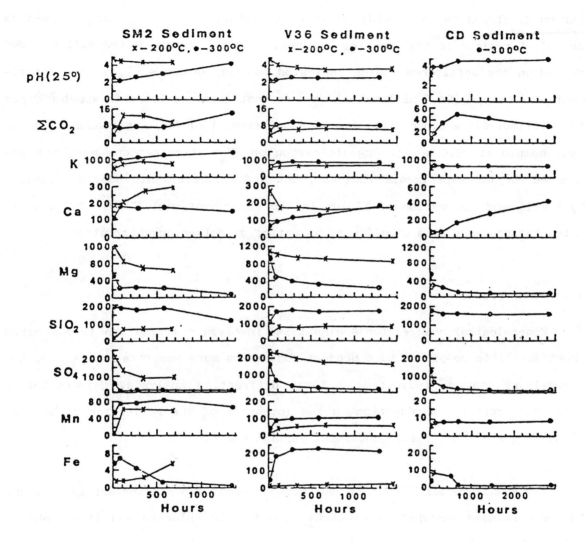

FIGURE 6.4. Change in concentration of aqueous components during experimental sediment-sea water interaction. All data in ppm except for CO_2 (millimolal) and pH.

$\underline{CO_2, C_{org}. \text{ and } CH_4}$. Total dissolved CO_2 increased in all experiments (Figure 6.4). In the experiments with sediments SM2 and V36 it rose to 10 millimolal or more while in the 300°C experiment with the diatomaceous ooze (CD) it reached a maximum concentration in excess of 50 millimolal. Coinciding with the evolution of CO_2 in the experiment with CD, a high content of dissolved organic carbon developed in the fluids as well as immiscible hydrocarbons observed as an "oily" residue in the sampling syringe. Organic carbon determinations per formed on the unfiltered fluids indicated maximum values early in the experiment of 1000 ppm (94.7 millimolal) or more that declined later to about 600 ppm (50 millimolal). A concentration of 1.63 millimolal of CH_4 was measured in the last sample at 2876 hours. Organic carbon or CH_4 determinations were not attempted for the experiments with V36, but a distinct organic odor accompanied by a yellowish coloration of fluids in the experiment with V36 at 300°C indicated the presence of a significant amount of dissolved organic matter.

Alteration Products

Mineralogical changes for sediment SM2 involved a transition from a mixed smectite-illite component to a product containing more smectite and less of the mixed-layer clay as indicated by X-ray diffraction analysis. Clinoptilolite dissolved entirely. A reduction in the intensity of the reflection of placioclase suggests that it also underwent partial reaction.

The abundances of SiO_2-rich amorphous material and plagioclase in sediment V36 were reduced somewhat as smectite formed while chlorite and illite showed little change. The organic carbon content of the sediment was found to decrease from 0.43% before reaction to 0.18% after reaction at 200°C and to 0.13% after reaction at 300°C. The total inorganic carbon concentrations of the experimental solutions (Table 6.2) are too low to account for the decrease in organic carbon observed. The aqueous concentrations of Fe and Mn are also lower than would be expected if ferromanganese oxyhydroxide phases had oxidized substan-

TABLE 6.2. CONCENTRATION OF MAJOR AQUEOUS COMPONENTS (ppm), TOTAL DISSOLVED CO_2 (MILLIMOLAL), AND pH DURING THERMAL GRADIENT EXPERIMENTS.

Smpl/hrs	pH	C_T	Na	K	Ca	Mg	SiO_2	SO_4	Cl
"Soret" experiment, 100°C ("cool" zone)									
SW/0	7.85	2.25	9214	359	359	1661	–	–	19994
1/1.0	7.18	–	9467	390	396	1644	–	–	20373
2/28.5	4.31	–	9577	393	393	1643	–	–	19654
3/99.0	5.80	–	9853	405	417	1698	–	–	21221
4/337.5	6.52	–	10323	449	441	1790	–	–	22321
5/503.5	6.40	–	10641	467	464	1837	–	–	22955
6/673.0	6.57	2.8	10838	475	481	1888	–	–	23423
"Soret" experiment, 300°C ("hot" zone)									
SW/0	7.85	2.25	9214	359	395	1661	–	–	19994
1/1.0	6.86	–	9140	388	371	1586	–	–	19654
2/28.5	6.90	–	9429	414	401	1501	–	–	19932
3/99.0	5.67	–	8788	365	378	1425	–	–	18684
5/503.5	5.31	–	5629	186	172	700	–	–	11186
6/673.0	5.58	3.3	4918	203	184	746	–	–	10244
Sediment gradient experiment, 100°C ("cool" zone)									
SW/0	7.9	2.33	10763	399	412	1297	<.2	2734	19375
1/21.5	6.02	3.45	11050	630	431	1235	247	2773	19900
2/101.5	5.62	3.93	11866	725	418	1232	397	2923	21144
3/284.5	5.39	4.07	13136	877	393	1206	566	2891	23179
4/504.5	5.31	4.33	13752	969	390	1182	599	2754	24249
Sediment gradient experiment, 300°C ("hot" zone)									
SW/0	7.9	2.33	10763	399	412	1297	<.2	2734	19375
1/21.5	7.88	2.59	11153	579	305	1162	51	2442	19764
2/101.5	5.00	13.12	11473	1077	223	254	626	442	19219
3/284.5	4.11	12.70	9621	833	152	142	833	239	15673
4/504.5	3.51	10.12	8158	652	113	129	781	226	13462

SW = Starting composition of artificial sea water in "Soret" experiment and Copenhagen sea water in sediment gradient experiment.

pH measured at 25°C; – not analyzed.

tial amounts of organic material. Thus, most of the decrease in organic carbon of the sediment is attributed to the loss of the organic carbon component by dissolution. This explanation is substantiated to some degree by the presence of an organic odor noted in the solution samples.

Sediment CD contained smectite after reaction with sea water at 300°C and cristobalite produced by precipitation of aqueous silica or by recrystallization of amorphous silica. A portion of the organic matter present underwent alteration by pyrolysis as indicated by the presence of CH_4 and CO_2 in the fluids sampled during the experiment and a color change in the sediment from the original olive to a dark gray at the end of the experiment. A substantial portion of the organic matter also was mobilized into the fluids by dissolution and colloidal suspension as indicated by the high organic content of the sampled fluids and the presence of liquid hydrocarbons.

Anhydrite was identified as an alteration product of all experiments, both microscopically and by X-ray diffraction.

Discussion

Chemical Exchange and pH Regulation During Sediment-Sea Water Interaction

Experiments in the sediment-sea water system at 200°C and 300°C indicate that acidity develops due to Mg removal from solution /8/. Bischoff and Seyfried /18/ have demonstrated that at temperatures above 250°C at 500 bars, sea water loses Mg due to the precipitation of Mg-hydroxysulfate hydrate. This mechanism for H^+ generation may be written as:

$$(n+1)Mg^{++} + nSO_4^= + (n-1)H_2O = MgO \cdot nMgSO_4 \cdot (n-2)H_2O + 2H^+ \qquad (6.1)$$

where 3 n 5. This reaction is probably important during the first few hours of an experiment. Sulfate also is removed from solution as anhydrite precipitates, however, and reaction (6.1) is soon superseded by reactions involving sea water Mg and $SiO_{2(aq)}$ derived from the dissolution of quartz and amorphous silica. This process can be illustrated by the reaction:

$$3Mg^{++} + 4SiO_{2(aq)} + 4H_2O = Mg_3Si_4O_{10}(OH)_2 + 6H^+ \qquad (6.2)$$

Thus, the formation of smectite either as a distinct phase or as talc interlayers within existing clay minerals is probably the most important mechanism for producing the acidity observed during these experiments. This process is substantiated by the observation that smectite is a dominant alteration product.

The length of time that solution pH remains acidic depends upon the sediment mineralogy. The reaction of carbonates or the hydrolysis of anhydrous silicate phases serves to titrate H^+ and pH will remain low only as long as enough Mg remains in solution to replace the H^+ consumed by reaction of these minerals. Thus in the experiment with sediment SM2 at 300°C, pH remained below 3 until reaction of clinoptilolite, illite, and a minor amount of calcareous and organic material resulted in partial neutralization of acidity and the removal of the bulk of Mg from solution (Figure 6.4). In contrast, the fluid chemistry of the experiment involving sediment V36 at 300°C remained acid due to the lack of reactive minerals, particularly calcareous material and K-bearing phases. The results of the experiments with these two sediments at 200°C further substantiate these deductions; note in particular the higher values of C_T, K and pH for SM2 relative to V36 and the rapidly concentrations of Mg and SO_4 in the experiment with SM2.

The experiment with diatomaceous ooze (CD) at 300°C also illustrates the importance of these types of reactions. The rapid rise in C_T and pH observed may be attributed to the reaction of calcareous material and the oxidation and pyrolysis of organic material (see below). The steady rise in the concentration of Ca and decline in C_T in the latter part of the experiment suggests that the hydrolysis of a Ca-silicate phase such as plagioclase may also have had an important role in controlling fluid chemistry.

The effect of sediment-sea water interaction on solution chemistry, including pH, can be graphically illustrated through the use of mineral-activity diagrams. These diagrams conveniently illustrate mineral stability fields relative to solution composition. Thus, their use can reveal a great deal concerning solution-mineral equilibria and alteration processes. As an example of this approach, mineral-activity diagrams for the $MgO-CaO-K_2O-Al_2O_3-SiO_2-H_2O$ system at 300°C, 500 bars, have been constructed using appropriate thermochemical data /9,10/; superimposed on these diagrams are the activity ratios of cations and H^+ calculated utilizing the solution data of the experiments at 300°C (Figure 6.5).

Computation ion activities of aqueous species was performed utilizing "SOLVEQ", a computer program written by Reed /11/. SOLVEQ distributes element concentrations among aqueous species through a series of mass balance equations containing dissociation constants for complexes and by assuming electrical neutrality. The extended Debye Huckle equation is utilized to compute activity coefficients /12/. Activities were first computed at 25°C and 1 bar using the measured pH. From initial distribution a hydrogen ion mass balance was computed for use in calculating activities at elevated temperatures and pressures. Hydrolysis constants of minerals at the experimental conditions calculated from the data of Helgeson et al. /10/ were compared with the activity products to determine the extent of saturation of the solutions with respect to selected minerals.

The reaction paths defined by the data illustrated in Figure 6.5 demonstrate that pH changes are related to mineralogical reactions involving the exchange of H^+ for Ca^{++}, Mg^{++} and K^+. The data from the experiment at 300°C with sediment SM2 clearly illustrates the general direction of the reaction path. Initially, the activity ratios decrease as H^+ is released into solution by the hydrolysis of water in conjunction with the formation of smectite (reaction 2); thus the activity ratios of the solution lie well within the stability field of

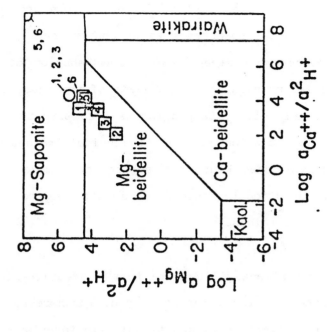

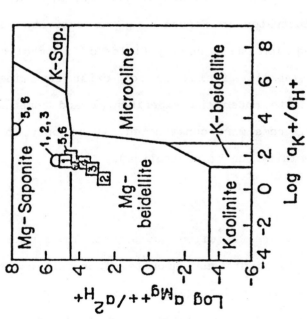

FIGURE 6.5. Mineral activity diagrams for the $MgO-CaO-K_2O-Al_2O_3-SiO_2-H_2O$ system at 300°C, 500 bars and amorphous silica saturation ($a_{SiO_2} = 10^{-1.48}$). Data points represent the activity ratios for solution samples (squares = SM2, 300°C; solid circle = V36, 300°C, 1297 hours; open circles = CD, 300°C).

- 111 -

Mg-beidellite, a dioctahedral smectite. The reaction path subsequently reverses as H^+ in solution is removed by the hydrolysis of the primary silicate minerals and the activity ratios move to the univariant boundary between Mg-beidellite and Mg-saponite, an analog for trioctahedral smectite. The experiment with sediment V36 demonstrates a similar, though less pronounced, evolution of solution chemistry and also appears to be constrained by the saponite-beidellite univariant boundary at steady state. The behavior of sediment CD, however, is somewhat different owing to the ability of the inorganic and organic carbon and volcanic debris (i.e., Ca-plagioclase) to titrate acidity. Thus, the activity ratios of the solution lie near the beidellite-saponite boundary during the first several hundred hours but subsequently move to higher cation/H^+ ratios after the solution is depleted of solution Mg to the point that acidity can no longer be maintained.

Thus, these three experiments illustrate that a smectite-rich mineralogy is stable during sediment-sea water interaction and, furthermore, may contribute to acidity through the formation of additional talc interlayers or discrete smectite phases. As illustrated in Figure 6.5, the activity ratios of these solutions are far removed from the stability fields of the zeolite and feldspar minerals and, indeed, stability fields do not exist for minerals such as chlorite, illite, or calcite under the experimental and compositional conditions for which these diagrams were constructed. It is only through reaction with these phases that acidity can be neutralized.

Redox Equilibria

MnO_2 and Fe_2O_3 phases are ubiquitous components of marine sediments and are commonly accompanied by significant amounts of organic carbon and ferrous iron, the latter incorporated in detrital material such as chlorite, volcanic debris, or magnetite. This assemblage induces vigorous redox reactions at elevated temperatures and pressures which greatly affect solution chemistry and alteration processes.

Reaction of MnO_2 with organic carbon and components containing ferrous iron can be illustrated as:

$$MnO_2 + CH_2O + 2H^+ = Mn^{2+} + CO_2 + H_2O \qquad (6.3)$$

and

$$MnO_2 + Fe_2SiO_4 + 2H^+ = Mn^{2+} + Fe_2O_3 + H_2O + SiO_{2(aq)} \qquad (6.4)$$

where CH_2O and Fe_2SiO_4 represent organic matter and ferrous iron phases respectively. Thus, pore solutions in sediment containing MnO_2 in excess of organic matter and ferrous iron will be characterized by high Mn concentrations and low Fe concentrations, and will have CO_2 concentrations proportional to the abundance of organic matter present. Sediments containing a larger amount of organic matter will ultimately reduce all MnO_2-containing phases and Fe_2O_3 will be the dominant oxidizing agent; that is, ferrous iron will enter solution in response to the reaction:

$$Fe_2O_3 + CH_2O + 4H^+ = 2Fe^{2+} + CO_2 + 2H_2O \qquad (6.5)$$

The experimental results presented are clearly influenced by the redox processes presented above. Reaction of sediment SM2 with sea water yielded distinctly oxidizing fluids characterized by high Mn/Fe ratios (Figure 6.4). This sediment contained a sufficient amount of MnO_2 to oxidize virtually all of the organic carbon (0.05%) and ferrous iron available (reactions 3 and 4). Sediment V36, in contrast, generated more reduced fluids characterized by relatively low Mn/Fe ratios owing to a relatively high organic carbon content (0.43%) and relative absence of MnO_2. Hematite thus acted as the primary oxidizing agent, releasing ferrous iron into solution as organic carbon was oxidized (reaction 5).

Reaction of the diatomaceous ooze CD with sea water at 300°C generated relatively reduced fluids similar to those from the V36 experiment. That is, they were characterized by high Fe and low Mn. In contrast to V36, however, CO_2 concentrations reached levels in excess of 50 millimolal. The extremely high organic carbon content (3.99%) of this sediment is largely responsible for this although the reaction of calcareous material may also have contributed CO_2.

Estimation of Oxygen Fugacity

Quantitative evaluation of the oxidation potential of these experiments is extremely difficult due to an inability to define the stable phases involved in redox equilibria as well as uncertainties in thermochemical data for the phases involved (e.g., hematite and pyrolusite). The solubility of Au from the reaction cell has proven generally useful in many experiments, however, because the redox couple involved is defined in terms of one phase (Au) and the aqueous Au complexes of which $AuCl_2^-$ is of primary importance. Thermodynamic data from Helgeson /12/ together with in situ activities calculated by SOLVEQ from the measured pH and concentrations of Au and Cl in the fluids may thus be utilized to calculate f_{O_2} from the following equilibria:

$$Au^0 + 2Cl^- + H^+ \ 1/4O_2 = AuCl_2^- + 1/2H_2O \qquad (6.6)$$

f_{O_2} was found to range in the experiment with the oxidized sediment SM2 from 10^{-13} to 10^{-17} at 300°C whereas that computed for the experiment with V36 at 300°C was about 10^{-20}, due to its moderately reduced nature (Figure 6.6).

The f_{O_2} of the experimental at 300°C with sediment CD could not be accurately assessed by the $Au-AuCl_2^-$ redox couple due to the low solubility of Au under the alkaline, reduced conditions present. During the first several samples, however, gold was approximately 0.05 ppm, the detection limit for this element. Utilizing this value for the first three fluid samples, a f_{O_2} of 10^{-20} was computed (Figure 6.6). This value thus represents a maximum oxygen fugacity. Another redox couple was employed subsequently as CH_4 was generated by the thermal alteration of the organic material present. Since the CO_2 concentration was also measured, it is possible to calculate f_{O_2} through the redox couple between these two components:

$$CO_2 + 2H_2O = CH_4 + 3/2 \ O_2 \qquad (6.7)$$

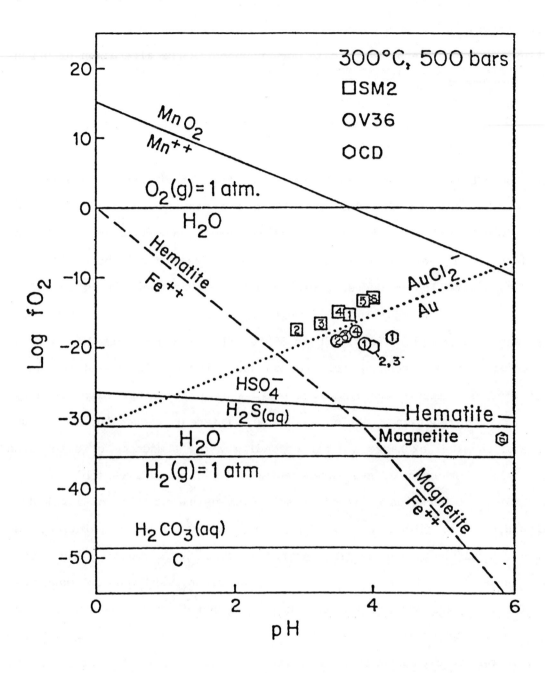

FIGURE 6.6. Relationship of redox couples and chemistry of experimental solution samples as a function of f_{O_2} and pH at 300°C, 500 bars. Boundaries drawn assuming an activity of 10^{-6} for aqueous species.

From this reaction, a f_{O_2} of 10^{-33} was calculated for sample 6 which contained 29.0 millimolal CO_2 and 1.63 millimolal CH_4 (Figure 6.4). Thus, sea water interaction with CD appears to have initially generated moderately oxidized fluids which subsequently became more reduced as the alteration of organic matter proceeded.

Low-Temperature Sea Water-Sediment Interaction

It should be clear from the previous discussion that the key (sensitive) parameters affecting radionuclide mobiliy in the near field geochemical environment (associated with high level waste disposal in deep ocean sediments) are solution pH, f_{O_2} and sediment mineralogy and chemistry. Although temperature, and to a much lesser degree pressure affects these parameters by influencing solution-mineral equilibria, steady state solution chemistry for sediment-sea water interaction from 100°C to 300°C will be characterized by similar directions of chemical exchange relative to sea water chemistry and the existence of similar silicate alteration phases. What will change significantly, however, will be reaction kinetics at these different temperatures and the magnitude of chemical exchange and correspondingly the abundance of alteration mineral phases. For example, sea water-sediment (quartz, illite-rich) interaction at 150°C, 500 bars (unpublished experimental data) results in slight Mg^{++} removal and K^+, Na^+, SiO_2, Fe^{++} and Mn^{+2} gains respectively in solution, and formation of small but nevertheless significant amounts of smectite and dissolution of equally small amounts of illite, plagiclase and iron and manganese oxides. These changes are similar to those outlined in detail above for sea water-sediment interaction at 200-300°C, 500 bars. Since the kinetics of reaction are faster at higher temperatures (this is illustrated by the rate and extent of Mg^{++} removal from solution) solution pH is often acid, owing to rapid smectite precipitation, and only slowly "titrated" by dissolution of primary detrital components in the sediment (plagioclase and illite). Phases such as kaolinite, which often constitute 20-30% of the sediment do not participate in acid neutralization because of their stability in relatively acidic fluids. In contrast, smectite precipitation at 100-150°C during sea water-sediment interaction is extremely slow (sluggish Mg^{++} removal from solution). Thus H^+ production is sufficiently slow for mineral dissolution reactions to "prevail" and a near neutral to slightly alkaline pH is achieved.

f_{O_2} is almost entirely a function of sediment mineralogy and chemistry. This is not to imply that f_{O_2} will not be influenced by temperature -- it will, but only in an absolute sense. The relative oxidative capacity of sediment will be uneffected by temperature. For example, fO_2 in equilibrium with a hematite-magnetite alteration assemblage at 300°C is approximately 10^{-28} atm, whereas the same assemblage supports an f_{O_2} of 10^{-68} atm at 25°C. In effect this represents temperature-dependent changes in the equilibrium constants for pertinent reaction. The effective redox state; that is, the extent to which sediment acts as an oxidizing or reducing agent with respect to a hydrothermal fluid or nuclear waste containing canister is controlled entirely by sediment chemistry and mineralogy.

Conclusions

1) Sea water-sediment interaction at 200-300°C, 500 bars results in generation of appreciable quantities of H^+ owing Mg-metasomatic affects -- these being characterized by Mg-smectite and hydroxysulfate formation. To avoid H^+ generation in analogous amounts in a natural sub-seabed repository, near field temperatures should not exceed 200°C.

2) In addition to removal of Mg^{++}, solutions from these experiments are characterized by losses in Ca^{++}, Sr^{+2} and $SO_4^=$ and gains in K^+, Na^+, $SiO_{2(aq)}$, Fe^{+2}, Mn^{2+} and total inorganic carbon relative to sea water chemistry. In general, these changes reflect smectite and anhydrite

formation and dissolution of detrital mineral phases, especially illite, chlorite, plagioclase feldspar, volcanic glass as well as siliceous skeletal fragments and assorted zeolite phases.

3) Mn^{+2} and Fe^{2+} concentration in solution were found to be important indicators of redox reactions taking place in the sediment. High concentrations of these species typically reflect the relative abundance of organic carbon and ferrous-iron bearing silicates in the sediment. Redox reactions can be assessed experimentally by use of the $Au-AuCl_2^-$ redox couple. This information integrated with estimates of solution pH and temperature can be employed to constrain estimates of canister and wasteform stability, and in general, the suitability of a particular site as a long term repository for high level radioactive waste.

4) Sediment-sea water interaction at temperature less than 200°C will be characterized by directions of chemical exchange and alteration mineralogy similar to that illustrated here at 200-300°C, but reaction kinetics will be quite different. The results of this are reflected by the absence of a distinct pH minimum during relatively low temperature (∿100-150°C) sea water-sediment interaction owing to a slow rate of smectite formation. The oxidative capacity of sediment will be relatively uneffected by temperature.

6.4 Thermal Gradient Experiments

Introduction

Most studies designed to date to study near field geochemistry have documented the effect of temperature on solution-mineral equilibria or the stability of various nuclear waste-forms and canister materials. Thus, a rather extensive database exists as a result of closed system experiments at constant temperature and pressure. However, these studies have, by their very design neglected the effect of thermal gradients on near field transport processes. Most notable in this regard is thermal diffusion, the so-called Soret effect, which appears to have received little or no consideration in any of the current models formulated for nuclear waste disposal in geologic media. An adequate understanding of this process is essential for the sub-seabed disposal concept, however, because of the inherently low permeability of marine pelagic clay and mass transport dominated by diffusion.

The objective of this facet of the report is to make available results of two thermal gradient experiments involving sea water and sediment. These experiments have been conducted to assess the degree and rate of separation of aqueous components in an appropriate thermal gradient. One of these, referred to throughout this report as the "Soret" experiment, was conducted utilizing powdered alumina and not naturally occurring sediment. The alumina behaved as an inert matrix and thus provided thermidiffusional data on mass transport in the absence of rock-water interaction effects. The other thermal gradient experiment contained sediment and provided data relevant to both diffusional and rock-water interaction processes. The sediment used for this experiment was identical to that used for one of the previously described constant temperature experiments namely the quartz-illite-chlorite(Fe)-amorphous silica-rich V36 sediment from the western North Pacific.

Results reviewed here are from experiments conducted in thermal gradient apparatus described in detail in Part I of this report. In general, reactants (alumina or sediment) were poured in the reaction cell (see Figures 6.2 and 6.3) as a water-rich slurry ($\sim$ 70 cc). The water/rock mass ratio was approximately 3.

After sealing the cell, air was evacuated and replaced by additional sea water introduced through the upper sampling valve, and the cell was transferred in an upright position and placed within a preheated furnace (Figure 6.3). A dual set-point, time proportioning controller (Omega Engineering) was utilized to maintain a constant furnace temperature. In the experiments conducted, conditions were attained in about 3 hours with the development of a 200°C temperature gradient; 300°C in the "hot" zone at the bottom of the cell to 100°C in the fluid overlying the sediment in the upper portion of the cell. An assembly of 5 external thermocouples emplaced in the exterior steel casing of the cell monitored the thermal gradient during the course of each experiment (Figure 6.2). These temperature measurements have been demonstrated to represent conditions internal to the reaction cell to $\pm$ 5°C. Pressure was maintained at 600 bars, except when sampling fluids (see below). The experiments were quenched after two to three months.

Solution samples from the thermal gradient experiments were obtained at intervals of one day, three days, one week, and subsequently every two to three weeks from the "hot" and "cool" zone of the thermal gradient reaction cell (see Figures 6.2 and 6.3). The procedure consisted of first obtaining a 2 ml sample from the "cool" zone by sampling "down pressure" from 600 bars to 100 bars. 0.5 mls of this fluid was used for analysis of inorganic carbon (C_T), while the remainder was used for determination of pH and for other aqueous components after filtering and acidifying with ultrapure HNO_3. The system was immediately repressurized to 600 bars by pumping unreacted sea water back into the "cool" zone via a separator. A bleed sample (~ 0.5 ml) was then immediately taken to clear the lower exit tube and another 2 ml sample was taken from the "hot" zone. Additional unreacted sea water was pumped into the "cool" zone while sampling the "hot" zone in order to maintain a pressure of 600 bars within the system. A test performed during the development of the system verified that any dilution of the "hot" zone sample by "cool" zone fluid was insignificant during the short period of time required for sampling.

As with constant temperature experiments sample aliquots were chemically processed by numerous analytical techniques /7/.

Results

Solution Chemistry

Fluid samples from the Soret experiment demonstrated that Cl, Na, K, Ca and Mg were depleted in the "hot" zone and enriched in the "cool" zone (Figure 6.7). pH values were slightly lower than for the unreacted fluid (7.85). C_T was enriched in the "hot" zone relative to the "cool" zone.

The concentrations of Cl, Na, Mg, Ca and SO_4 were depleted in the "hot" zone of the sediment gradient experiment relative to the "cool" zone (Table 6.3) and Figure 6.7. K was initially higher in the "hot" zone but later became depleted in the "hot" zone relative to the "cool" zone. Both zones were enriched in K relative to the starting fluid and depleted in Ca and Mg (Figure 7) and in SO_4. C_T and silica were enriched in the "hot" zone relative to the "cool" zone. pH (25°C) was initially higher in the "hot" zone than in the "cool" zone (21.5 hours) but subsequently became more acidic in the "hot" zone. All samples were more acidic than Copenhagen sea water except for the first sample from the "hot" zone. Fe, Mn and Zn attained maximum values of 239, 152 and 14 ppm, respectively, in the "hot" zone (Table 6.3). Mn increased steadily to a maximum values of 66 ppm in the "cool" zone while Fe and Zn were below detection limits. B and Ba were enriched in the "hot" zone relative to the "cool" zone while Sr was enriched in the "cool" zone (Table 6.3).

Alteration Products

X-ray diffraction analysis of reacted sediment from the "hot" zone ($\sim 300°C$) of the thermal gradient experiment with sediment V36 showed no miner-

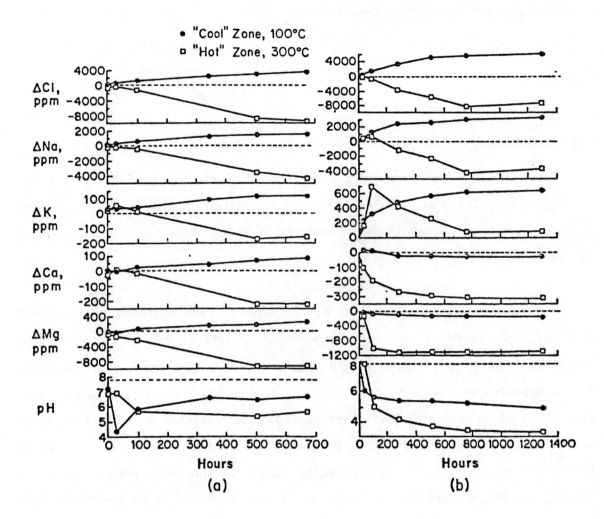

FIGURE 6.7. Change in fluid composition of "hot" and "cool" zones of (a) "Soret" and (b) sediment thermal gradient experiments with time relative to starting fluid composition.

alogical changes other than the production of anhydrite and a minor increase in chlorite relative to illite (based on the intensities of the 14A and 10A diffraction peaks, respectively).

Discussion

Thermal Diffusion and Sediment-Sea Water Interaction

The solution data obtained from the thermal gradient experiments reviewed here may be utilized to quantify the magnitude of the Soret effect in the near field marine enviroment. The total flux of solute in a system is the algebraic sum of the flux due to thermal diffusion, the flux due to a chemical gradient (i.e., chemical or Fickian diffusion), and the flux contributed by rock-water interaction,

$$F = -D \frac{dC}{dz} - D_T C \frac{dT}{dz} + R \qquad (6.8)$$

where F is the net flux of a solute component, D is the coefficient of chemical diffusion, DT is the coefficient of thermal diffusion, C is the concentration of a solute component, T is temperature, z is distance and R is a hypothetical component describing the flux contributed by rock-water interaction /13/.

If rock-water interaction is negligible (i.e. R = 0) equation (6.8) may also be expressed as

$$F = -D \left(\frac{dC}{dz} + sC \frac{dT}{dz} \right) \qquad (6.9)$$

where

$$s = \frac{D_T}{D} \qquad (6.10)$$

The symbol $s(°C^{-1})$ is the Soret coefficient which is defined as a positive quantity by equation (6.9).

If a system is at steady state and if $R \sim 0$, the fluxes generated by thermal and chemical diffusion will be balanced and the next flux zero. Thus equation (6.9) becomes

$$s = -\frac{1}{C}\frac{dC}{dT} \tag{6.11}$$

This expression has generally been utilized to calculate Soret coefficients from experimental data in previous studies. By rearranging this expression and integrating over the limits of concentration and temperature, however, it will be noted that

$$\Delta \ln C = -s\, \Delta T \tag{6.12}$$

Equation (6.12) is more useful than equation (6.11) because it is indepent of the mean concentration of the system, a quantity that would be difficult to precisely evaluate in the system being considered. Equation (6.12) may be utilized to obtain values for the Soret coefficient of solute components by plotting the aqueous concentrations from the experiments relative to temperature on a semilogaritmic scale and measuring the slope of a best fit line drawn through the data. Values for the Soret coefficient derived utilizing this approach are presented in Table 6.4.

The data presented here appears to be the first reported for Soret coeficients in aqueous media at temperatures above 50°C and the only data available for sea water. Moreover, the absence of a general theory describing thermal diffusion prevents accurate extrapolation of data obtained at lower temperatures to the temperatures of these experiments or to predict values of complex electrolyte solutions (i.e. seawater) from that of binary electrolyte solutions. The constraint of electrical neutrality, however, obviously must be important in complex electrolyte solutions. Thus, the Soret coefficients obtained for various components in sea water may be influenced to a large degree by the dominant components present, Na and Cl. This may serve to explain the similarity of Soret values reported for the various components of the "Soret" experiment (Table 6.4). An evaluation of existing literature data for NaCl solutions in the range of sea water concentrations may therefore be appropriate.

Caldwell /13/ and Caldwell and Eide /15/ have measured Soret coefficients for 0.5 N NaCl solutions at temperatures from 0° to approximately 500°C and at pressures from 1 to 700 bars (Figure 6.8). These data can be used to assess the pressure dependence of Soret coefficients, at conditions appropriate to model thermodiffusional process for subseabed disposal of high level radioactive waste. The temperature dependence of the Soret coefficient is restricted to less than 50°C (Figure 6.8), but based on the linear relation noted by Caldwell /16/ for the Soret coefficient for NaCl solutions of sea water ionic strength and the coefficient of thermal expansion (Figure 6.9), estimates for Soret coefficients can be obtained for higher temperature. Since the coefficient of isobaric thermal expansion increases logarithmically with temperature, then the Soret coefficient should exhibit a similar functional relation to temperature. This is precisely what was observed by Caldwell /16/ when the experimentally determined Soret Coefficient for 0.5 N NaCl was plotted as a function of temperature to 50°C (Figure 9B). It should be noted that the Soret coefficients computed for Cl ($0.0040°C^{-1}$) and Na ($0.0040°C^{-1}$) obtained from the "Soret" experiment mentioned earlier are consistent with this functional relationship (see Figure 6.8).

Comparison of the values of the Soret coefficient for Cl, Na, Mg, K and Ca from the two experiments presented above may be utilized to evaluate the extent to which rock-water interaction contributes to the net solute flux in these

TABLE 6.3. CONCENTRATIONS OF MINOR ELEMENTS (ppm) IN FLUID SAMPLES COLLECTED DURING THE SEDIMENT THERMAL GRADIENT EXPERIMENT.

Smp/hrs	Fe	Mn	Zn	Ba	Sr	Al	B	U	Cs	Mo
100°C ("cool" zone)										
SW/0	<.01	<.01	<.01	0.03	7.9	<.01	4.4	< 5	<.1	< 1
1/21.5	< 1	19	< 3	< 2	8.5	<.5	6.5	< 5	<.1	< 1
2/101.5	2	35	3	< 2	8.5	<.5	7.1	< 5	0.2	< 1
3.284.5	< 1	53	< 3	< 2	7.3	<.5	8.5	< 5	0.4	< 1
4/504.5	< 1	67	< 3	< 2	7.0	0.5	8.9	< 5	0.2	< 1
5/768.0	< 1	79	–	–	6.8	–	9.3	< 6	0.2	< 1
6/1296.0	< 1	95	–	–	–	–	–	–	–	–
Q/1302.0	11	79	–	–	–	–	–	–	–	–
300°C ("hot" zone)										
SW/0	<.01	<.01	<.01	0.03	7.9	<.01	4.4	< 5	<.1	< 1
1/21.5	< 1	6	< 3	< 2	6.0	<.5	5.8	< 5	<.1	< 1
2/101.5	176	161	14	5	3.6	<.5	17.5	–	<.1	< 1
3/284.5	183	128	12	< 2	2.4	<.5	15.2	< 5	<.1	< 1
4/504.5	120	99	5	2	0.6	<.5	11.1	< 5	<.1	< 1
5/768.0	90	84	–	–	< 2	–	9.4	< 5	<.1	< 1
6/1296.0	89	79	–	–	–	–	–	–	–	–

TABLE 6.4. SORET COEFFICIENTS (10^{-3}/°C) OF SELECTED COMPONENTS DERIVED FROM EXPERIMENTAL FLUID DATA.

	a) "Soret" experiment	b) Sediment experiment
Cl	4.1	2.9
Na	4.0	2.6
Mg	4.6	11.1
K	4.3	2.0
Ca	4.8	6.2

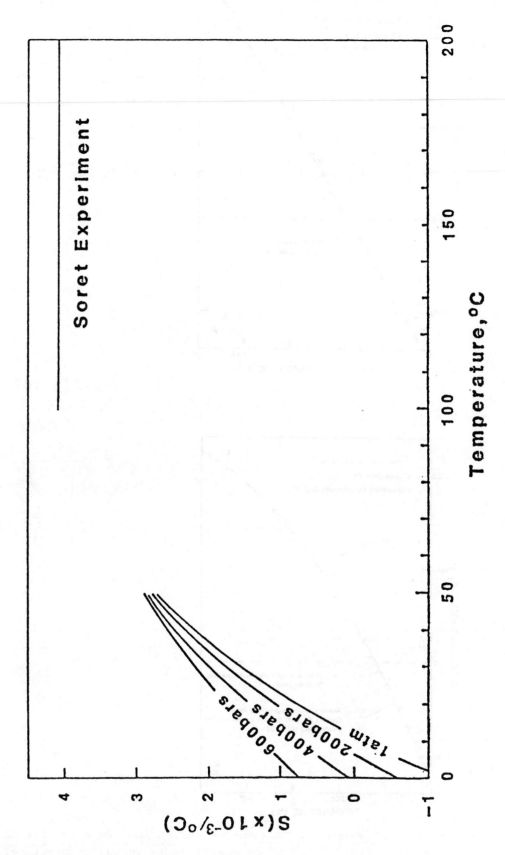

FIGURE 6.8.   Variation of the Soret coefficient for 0.5 N NaCl solution as a function of pressure (1 atm to 600 bars) and temperature (0° to 50°C) after Caldwell and Eide (1981). Also shown is the Soret coefficient for Cl obtained from the "Soret" experiment (100° to 300°C, 600 bars.

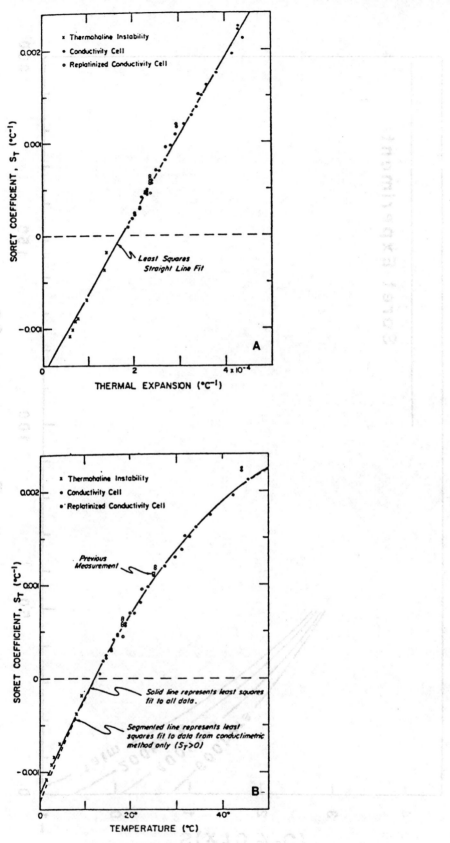

FIGURE 6.9. (A) Soret coefficients versus thermal expansion. Data and figure from Caldwell (1973). (B) Soret coefficients versus temperature. Data and figure from Caldwell (1973).

systems. Thus, the Soret coefficients obtained from the "Soret" experiment may be regarded as "pure" values since rock-water interaction was not involved while Soret coefficients derived from the sediment gradient experiment and from the simulation are "apparent" due to a contribution from rock-water interaction (i.e. R = O in equation (6.8)).

Soret coefficients for Cl are nearly identical for the "Soret" experiment, and the sediment experiment (Table 6.4). This observation suggests that Cl fluxes were controlled primarily by diffusional processes with little or no contribution to Cl flux by rock-water interaction. Also, Na appears to have been fairly inert during these experiments judging from the similarity of Soret coefficients, though slightly lower values in the experiments conducted with sediment suggest that some Na was released in the "hot" zone by rock-water interaction.

The relatively high values for the Soret coefficient of Mg in the sediment gradient experiment compared to that of the "Soret" experiment implies that Mg was removed from solution in the "hot" zone by rock-water interaction processes, presumably in response to smectite formation.

The sediment gradient experiment was also characterized initially by a higher pH in the "hot" zone than in the "cool" zone (Figure 6.7) but became more acidic in the "hot" zone after approximately 100 hours. This behavior may be ascribed to the closed system geometry of the sediment gradient experiment. Most striking in this regard is the rapid buildup of silica in the "cool" zone fluid due to chemical and thermal diffusion. The high concentration of silica in the "cool" zone permitted higher concentrations to accumulate, as well in the "hot" zone, which led to smectite precipitation. Thus, Mg diffused back towards the "hot" zone (Figure 6.7) and the generated H^+ by precipitation of Mg-bearing phases (smectite).

Ca and K appear to have also been involved in water-rock interaction during the sediment gradient experiment. Thus, the large values of the "apparent" Soret coefficient for Ca (Table 6.4) indicates that this component was removed from the fluids in the "hot" zone. Furthermore, examination of Figure 6.7 illustrates that the "cool" zone of this experiment was being depleted of Ca due to the precipitation of anhydrite in the "hot" zone. In contrast, relatively small values for the "apparent" Soret coefficient of K in the sediment gradient experiment indicates that K was released into solution in the "hot" zone, presumably due to illite dissolution. Thus, Figure 6.7 illustrates a rapid increase in K concentration in the "hot" zone of the sediment gradient experiment during the first 100 hours followed by a depletion in the "hot" zone as K was transported towards the "cool" zone.

Finally, it is important to emphasize from the above discussion, as well as from other experimental studies bearing on thermodiffusional fluxes in electrolyte fluids, the steady state concentration gradient developed in the presence of the constant temperature gradient is small unless the thermal gradient is relatively large. This results from the fact that the thermal diffusion coefficient is typically smaller by a fraction of 10^2 to 10^3 than the ordinary diffusion coefficient. Thus the zone in the vicinity of a buried waste containing canister in subseabed sediment affected by thermodiffusion will be a strict function of the thermal gradient. For the seabed option envisaged for Europe, where high level waste storage will presumably be the norm rather than the exception, relatively low near field temperatures will constrain greatly thermodiffusional transport. For example, assuming a near field temperature of 150°C, an average Soret coefficient of 3×10^{-3} and a reasonable value for sediment thermal conductivity, a concentration gradient of only 0.15 m will occur, and this will be restricted to a zone within approximately 2-3 cm of the canister. Although this may affect alteration mineralogy in the near field, it will not contribute greatly as a mechanism of radionuclide mobiliy.

Separation of Aqueous Species in a Thermal Gradient

In the discussion above, Soret coefficients were presented for five components (Na, Cl, Mg, K, Ca) without regard to how these components are distributed between various aqueous species. To investigate the extent to which individual species are separated in a thermal gradient, the aqueous data from the experiments was utilized to calculate the concentration of species at the appropriate temperatures using SOLVEQ. As noted previously SOLVEQ is a computer code permitting aqueous species distribution at elevated temperature and pressure.

Table 6.5 is a listing of the species concentrations in the "hot" and "cool" zone fluids of the "Soret" experiment at 673 hours and the calculated value of the Soret coefficient for each species. Of particular interest are the values for Na^+, Cl^-, Mg^{++}, K^+ and Ca^{++}. These species all have values of about 0.0048. The Soret values computed from the total concentrations of these components (Table 6.3) are all less than 0.0048, except for Ca. This observation can be attributed to the higher degree of complexation in the "hot" zone than in the "cool" zone, particularly for Na, Cl and K which are complexed to a significant degree as the aqueous species KCl, NaCl and HCl. The degree of complexation is not sufficient for these five components to significantly change the conclusions presented earlier with regard to rock-water interaction, however.

The pH and the carbonate concentrations of the "hot" and "cool" zones, in contrast, appear to be closely related to complexation. The total carbonate of the "hot" zone of the "Soret" experiment is greater and is comprised mainly of H_2CO_3 while the "cool" zone is comprised of HCO_3^- and other carbonate complexes. Most of the H^+ is also complexed; thus, the pH of the "hot" and "cool" zone must be controlled to a large degree by the separation of these complexes between these zones. A factor also contributing to free H^+ in the "hot" zone is

TABLE 6.5.   SPECIATION OF "HOT" AND "COOL" ZONE FLUIDS FROM THE "SORET" EXPERI-
MENT AND THE SORET COEFFICIENTS OF INDIVIDUAL AQUEOUS SPECIES.

	"Cool" (100°C)	"Hot" (300°C)	Soret coefficient
H^+	.42E-6*	.22E-4	-.020
Cl^-	.64	.24	.0049
HCO_3^-	.13E-2	.34E-5	.030
Ca^{++}	.12E-1	.46E-2	.0048
Mg^{++}	.77E-1	.30E-1	.0047
K^+	.12E-1	.46E-2	.0048
Na^+	.45	.16	.0052
OH^-	.26E-5	.17E-5	.0021
KCl	.89E-4	.60E-3	-.0095
$NaCl$	.20E-1	.53E-1	-.0049
$NaCO_3^-$	.13E-5	.13E-11	.069
$CaCO_3$	.21E-5	.12E-9	.049
$CaHCO_3^+$	.12E-3	.14E-4	.011
$MgCO_3$	.10E-4	.36E-9	.051
$MgHCO_3^+$	.66E-3	.45E-4	.013
$CO_3^=$	.13E-5	.45E-11	.063
H_2CO_3	.66E-3	.32E-2	-.0079
HCl	.13E-9	.19E-4	-.060
$MgOH^+$	.62E-4	.69E-3	-.012
$CaOH^+$	.35E-6	.21E-4	-.020

* Concentration in modal units.

the greater stability of hydroxide complexes and, consequently, the precipitation of hydroxide phases such as brucite.

Conclusions

The results of the thermal gradient experiments considered in this part of our report demonstrate that fluid chemistry of the near field environment will be determined by a combination of water-rock interaction and diffusional effects. Of particular importance with respect to a thermal gradient is thermal diffusion which creates concentration gradients through large scale and relatively rapid fluxes of aqueous components from the "hot" zone towards the "cool" zone. The result of this process is an "unmixing" event which decreases markedly the ionic strength of the "hot" zone through the removal of a large proportion of Na and Cl and increases pH and alkalinity through the removal of Mg, H^+ and SiO_2. Mg, Ca, K, SiO_2, SO_4 and the minor elements, however, appear to be influenced by rock-water interaction as well as by thermal diffusion.

Assessment of these processes is critical to the modelling of the near field environment, not only with regard to subseabed disposal of nuclear waste, but also for any of the disposal options that would employ containment within geological media of low permeability /17/. Among the factors that require consideration are the effects of thermal diffusion on rates of canister corrosion, waste form stability and near field/far field interaction. This latter point may change significantly conclusions drawn from low-temperature radionuclide adsorption studies, since near field fluid chemistry may be influenced to some degree by diffusional transport between the near and far field regions.

References

/1/ Hollister, C.D. (1977). The seabed option. Oceanus Vol. 20, No. 1, pp. 18-25.

/2/ Silva, A.J. (1977). Physical processes in deep-sea clays. Oceanus Vol. 20, No. 1, pp. 31-40.

/3/ Heath, G.R. (1981). Site qualification and multibarrier assessment. Subseabed Disposal Annual Report. January to December 1980, Sandia National Laboratories, Albuquerque, N.M.

/4/ Dickson, F.W., Blount, C.W. and Tunell, G. (1963). Use of hydrothermal solution equipement to determine the solubility of anhydrite in water from 100°C to 275°C and from 1 bar to 1000 bars pressures. Am. J. Sci., Vol. 261, pp. 61-78.

/5/ Seyfried, W.E. Jr., Gordon, P.C. and Dickson, F.W. (1979). A new reaction cell for hydrothermal solution equipment. Am. Mineralogist, Vol. 64, pp. 646-649.

/6/ Seyfried, W.E. Jr. and Mottl, M.J. (1982). Hydrothermal alteration of basalt by sea water under sea water-dominated conditions. Geochim. Cosmochim. Acta, Vol. 46, pp. 985-1002.

/7/ Seyfried, W.E. Jr and Dibble, W.E. Jr. (1980). Seawater-peridotite interaction at 300°C and 500 bars. Implications for the origin of oceanic serpentinites, Geochim. cosmochim. Cosmochim. Acta, Vol. 45, pp. 135-147.

/8/ Seyfried, W.E., Thornton, E.C. and Janecky, D.R. (1980). Sea water-sediment interaction at 300°C, 500 bars. Implications for seabed disposal of nuclear wastes. Proc. 3rd Int. Sym. on Water-Rock Interaction, Edmonton, Canada, pp. 135-137.

/9/ Wolery, T.J. (1978). Some chemical aspects of hydrothermal processes at mid-oceanic ridges - A theoretical study. Ph.D. Thesis, Northwestern University, Evanston, Illinois, pp. 263.

/10/ Helgeson, H.C., Delany, J.M., Nesbitt, H.W. and Bird, D.K. (1978). Summary and critique of the thermodynamic properties of rock-forming minerals. Am. J. Sci., Vol. 278-A, pp. 229.

/11/ Reed, M.H. (1977). Calculation of hydrothermal metasomatism and ore deposition in submarine volcanic rocks with special refernce to the West Shasta district. California, Ph.D. Thesis, University of California, Berkeley, pp. 107.

/12/ Helgeson, H.C. (1969). Thermodynamics of hydrothermal systems at elevated temperatures and pressures. Am. J. Sci., Vol. 267, pp. 729-804.

/13/ Lerman, A. (1979). Geochemical Processes. Wiley, New York, p. 96.

/14/ Caldwell, D.R. (1974). Thermal conductivity of sea water. Deep-Sea Research, Vol. 21, pp. 131-137.

/15/ Caldwell, D.R. and Eide, S.A. (1981). Soret coefficients and isothermal diffusivity of aqueous solutions of five principal salt constituents of sea water. Deep-sea Drilling Research, Vol. 28A, pp. 1605-1618.

/16/ Caldwell, D.R. (1973). Thermal and fickian diffusion of sodium chloride in a solution of oceanic concentration. Deep Sea Research, Vol. 20, pp. 1029-1039.

/17/ Thornton, E.C. and Seyfried, W.E. Jr. (1982). The Soret effect. Potential for thermodiffusional transport in a nuclear waste repository, Geol. Soc. America with Programs, Vol. 14, pp. 631-632.

/18/ Bischoft, J.L. and Seyfried, W.E. (1978). Hydrothermal chemistry of sea water from 25° to 350°C. Am. J. Sci., Vol. 178, pp. 838-860.

NEAR FIELD TASK GROUP

FINAL REPORT

Ed. F. Lanza

Members of the Group:

F. Lanza
CEC, Task Group Leader

R.B. Deagle
H.S. Sandia

J.A.C. Marples
U.K., Harwell

G.P. Marsh
U.K., Harwell

P. Van Iseghem
Belgium, CSK/CEN

WHERE TO OBTAIN OECD PUBLICATIONS
OÙ OBTENIR LES PUBLICATIONS DE L'OCDE

ARGENTINA - ARGENTINE
Carlos Hirsch S.R.L.,
Florida 165, 4º Piso,
(Galeria Guemes) 1333 Buenos Aires
Tel. 33.1787.2391 y 30.7122

AUSTRALIA - AUSTRALIE
D.A. Book (Aust.) Pty. Ltd.
11-13 Station Street (P.O. Box 163)
Mitcham, Vic. 3132   Tel. (03) 873 4411

AUSTRIA - AUTRICHE
OECD Publications and Information Centre,
4 Simrockstrasse,
5300 Bonn (Germany)   Tel. (0228) 21.60.45
Gerold & Co., Graben 31, Wien 1 Tel. 52.22.35

BELGIUM - BELGIQUE
Jean de Lannoy,
Avenue du Roi 202
B-1060 Bruxelles   Tel. (02) 538.51.69

CANADA
Renouf Publishing Company Ltd/
Éditions Renouf Ltée,
1294 Algoma Road, Ottawa, Ont. K1B 3W8
Tel: (613) 741-4333
Toll Free/Sans Frais:
Ontario, Quebec, Maritimes:
1-800-267-1805
Western Canada, Newfoundland:
1-800-267-1826
Stores/Magasins:
61 rue Sparks St., Ottawa, Ont. K1P 5A6
Tel: (613) 238-8985
211 rue Yonge St., Toronto, Ont. M5B 1M4
Tel: (416) 363-3171
Federal Publications Inc.,
301-303 King St. W.,
Toronto, Ont. M5V 1J5   Tel. (416)581-1552
Les Éditions la Liberté inc.,
3020 Chemin Sainte-Foy,
Sainte-Foy, P.Q. GIX 3V6, Tel. (418)658-3763

DENMARK - DANEMARK
Munksgaard Export and Subscription Service
35, Nørre Søgade, DK-1370 København K
Tel. +45.1.12.85.70

FINLAND - FINLANDE
Akateeminen Kirjakauppa,
Keskuskatu 1, 00100 Helsinki 10   Tel. 0.12141

FRANCE
OCDE/OECD
Mail Orders/Commandes par correspondance :
2, rue André-Pascal,
75775 Paris Cedex 16   Tel. (1) 45.24.82.00
Bookshop/Librairie : 33, rue Octave-Feuillet
75016 Paris
Tel. (1) 45.24.81.67 or/ou (1) 45.24.81.81
Librairie de l'Université,
12a, rue Nazareth,
13602 Aix-en-Provence   Tel. 42.26.18.08

GERMANY - ALLEMAGNE
OECD Publications and Information Centre,
4 Simrockstrasse,
5300 Bonn   Tel. (0228) 21.60.45

GREECE - GRÈCE
Librairie Kauffmann,
28, rue du Stade, 105 64 Athens Tel. 322.21.60

HONG KONG
Government Information Services,
Publications (Sales) Office,
Information Services Department
No. 1, Battery Path, Central

ICELAND - ISLANDE
Snæbjörn Jónsson & Co., h.f.,
Hafnarstræti 4 & 9,
P.O.B. 1131 – Reykjavik
Tel. 13133/14281/11936

INDIA - INDE
Oxford Book and Stationery Co.,
Scindia House, New Delhi 110001
Tel. 331.5896/5308
17 Park St., Calcutta 700016   Tel. 240832

INDONESIA - INDONÉSIE
Pdii-Lipi, P.O. Box 3065/JKT.Jakarta
Tel. 583467

IRELAND - IRLANDE
TDC Publishers - Library Suppliers,
12 North Frederick Street, Dublin 1
Tel. 744835-749677

ITALY - ITALIE
Libreria Commissionaria Sansoni,
Via Benedetto Fortini 120/10,
50125 Firenze   Tel. 055/645415
Via Bartolini 29, 20155 Milano   Tel. 365083
La diffusione delle pubblicazioni OCSE viene
assicurata dalle principali librerie ed anche da :
Editrice e Libreria Herder,
Piazza Montecitorio 120, 00186 Roma
Tel. 6794628
Libreria Hœpli,
Via Hœpli 5, 20121 Milano   Tel. 865446
Libreria Scientifica
Dott. Lucio de Biasio "Aeiou"
Via Meravigli 16, 20123 Milano   Tel. 807679

JAPAN - JAPON
OECD Publications and Information Centre,
Landic Akasaka Bldg., 2-3-4 Akasaka,
Minato-ku, Tokyo 107   Tel. 586.2016

KOREA - CORÉE
Kyobo Book Centre Co. Ltd.
P.O.Box: Kwang Hwa Moon 1658,
Seoul   Tel. (REP) 730.78.91

LEBANON - LIBAN
Documenta Scientifica/Redico,
Edison Building, Bliss St.,
P.O.B. 5641, Beirut   Tel. 354429-344425

MALAYSIA/SINGAPORE -
MALAISIE/SINGAPOUR
University of Malaya Co-operative Bookshop
Ltd.,
7 Lrg 51A/227A, Petaling Jaya
Malaysia   Tel. 7565000/7565425
Information Publications Pte Ltd
Pei-Fu Industrial Building,
24 New Industrial Road No. 02-06
Singapore 1953   Tel. 2831786, 2831798

NETHERLANDS - PAYS-BAS
SDU Uitgeverij
Christoffel Plantijnstraat 2
Postbus 20014
2500 EA's-Gravenhage   Tel. 070-789911
Voor bestellingen: Tel. 070-789880

NEW ZEALAND - NOUVELLE-ZÉLANDE
Government Printing Office Bookshops:
Auckland: Retail Bookshop, 25 Rutland Stseet,
Mail Orders, 85 Beach Road
Private Bag C.P.O.
Hamilton: Retail: Ward Street,
Mail Orders, P.O. Box 857
Wellington: Retail, Mulgrave Street, (Head
Office)
Cubacade World Trade Centre,
Mail Orders, Private Bag
Christchurch: Retail, 159 Hereford Street,
Mail Orders, Private Bag
Dunedin: Retail, Princes Street,
Mail Orders, P.O. Box 1104

NORWAY - NORVÈGE
Narvesen Info Center – NIC,
Bertrand Narvesens vei 2,
P.O.B. 6125 Etterstad, 0602 Oslo 6
Tel. (02) 67.83.10, (02) 68.40.20

PAKISTAN
Mirza Book Agency
65 Shahrah Quaid-E-Azam, Lahore 3 Tel. 66839

PHILIPPINES
I.J. Sagun Enterprises, Inc.
P.O. Box 4322 CPO Manila
Tel. 695-1946, 922-9495

PORTUGAL
Livraria Portugal, Rua do Carmo 70-74,
1117 Lisboa Codex   Tel. 360582/3

SINGAPORE/MALAYSIA -
SINGAPOUR/MALAISIE
See "Malaysia/Singapor". Voir
«Malaisie/Singapour»

SPAIN - ESPAGNE
Mundi-Prensa Libros, S.A.,
Castelló 37, Apartado 1223, Madrid-28001
Tel. 431.33.99
Libreria Bosch, Ronda Universidad 11,
Barcelona 7   Tel. 317.53.08/317.53.58

SWEDEN - SUÈDE
AB CE Fritzes Kungl. Hovbokhandel,
Box 16356, S 103 27 STH,
Regeringsgatan 12,
DS Stockholm   Tel. (08) 23.89.00
Subscription Agency/Abonnements:
Wennergren-Williams AB,
Box 30004, S104 25 Stockholm Tel. (08)54.12.00

SWITZERLAND - SUISSE
OECD Publications and Information Centre,
4 Simrockstrasse,
5300 Bonn (Germany)   Tel. (0228) 21.60.45
Librairie Payot,
6 rue Grenus, 1211 Genève 11
Tel. (022) 31.89.50
Maditec S.A.
Ch. des Palettes 4
1020 – Renens/Lausanne   Tel. (021) 35.08.65
United Nations Bookshop/Librairie des Nations-
Unies
Palais des Nations, 1211 – Geneva 10
Tel. 022-34-60-11 (ext. 48 72)

TAIWAN - FORMOSE
Good Faith Worldwide Int'l Co., Ltd.
9th floor, No. 118, Sec.2, Chung Hsiao E. Road
Taipei   Tel. 391.7396/391.7397

THAILAND - THAILANDE
Suksit Siam Co., Ltd., 1715 Rama IV Rd.,
Samyam Bangkok 5   Tel. 2511630
INDEX Book Promotion & Service Ltd.
59/6 Soi Lang Suan, Ploenchit Road
Patjumamwan, Bangkok 10500
Tel. 250-1919, 252-1066

TURKEY - TURQUIE
Kültur Yayinlari Is-Türk Ltd. Sti.
Atatürk Bulvari No: 191/Kat. 21
Kavaklidere/Ankara   Tel. 25.07.60
Dolmabahce Cad. No: 29
Besiktas/Istanbul   Tel. 160.71.88

UNITED KINGDOM - ROYAUME-UNI
H.M. Stationery Office,
Postal orders only: (01)211-5656
P.O.B. 276, London SW8 5DT
Telephone orders: (01) 622.3316, or
Personal callers:
49 High Holborn, London WC1V 6HB
Branches at: Belfast, Birmingham,
Bristol, Edinburgh, Manchester

UNITED STATES - ÉTATS-UNIS
OECD Publications and Information Centre,
2001 L Street, N.W., Suite 700,
Washington, D.C. 20036 - 4095
Tel. (202) 785.6323

VENEZUELA
Libreria del Este,
Avda F. Miranda 52, Aptdo. 60337,
Edificio Galipan, Caracas 106
Tel. 951.17.05/951.23.07/951.12.97

YUGOSLAVIA - YOUGOSLAVIE
Jugoslovenska Knjiga, Knez Mihajlova 2,
P.O.B. 36, Beograd   Tel. 621.992

Orders and inquiries from countries where
Distributors have not yet been appointed should be
sent to:
OECD, Publications Service, 2, rue André-Pascal,
75775 PARIS CEDEX 16.

Les commandes provenant de pays où l'OCDE n'a
pas encore désigné de distributeur doivent être
adressées à :
OCDE, Service des Publications. 2, rue André-
Pascal, 75775 PARIS CEDEX 16.

72233-12-1988

OECD PUBLICATIONS, 2, rue André-Pascal, 75775 PARIS CEDEX 16 - No. 44598 1988
PRINTED IN FRANCE
(66 88 16 1) ISBN 92-64-13171-X